EENY, MEENY, MINEY, MO—AND STILL-MO

EENY, MEENY, MINEY, MO –
and STILL-MO

Lessons in Living
from Five Frisky Red Squirrels

by

SAM CAMPBELL
The Philosopher of the Forest

Cover illustration by Lars Justinen
Inside illustrations by Will Forrest

A.B. Publishing, Inc.
Ithaca MI

Cover Artist:
James Converse

Cover Designer:
Chrystique Neibauer

Printed in the United States of America

Published by:
A. B. Publishing, Inc.
Ithaca, MI 48847
www.abpub.com

TO DUKE

TABLE OF CONTENTS

I	Eeny, Meeny, Miney, Mo—	9
II	—And Still-Mo!	27
III	Bad Dream Ahead	35
IV	To Make a Long Tail Short	40
V	God Be with You, Duke!	54
VI	When the Dumb Speak	59
VII	Just Make Yourselves at Home	65
VIII	C/O Postmaster, San Francisco	74
IX	Not-So-Good Neighbor Policy	77
X	A Letter from Duke	84
XI	Peanut Problem	87
XII	A Hole in Nothing	93
XIII	One False Step	101
XIV	"Missing in Action"	110
XV	Winter Ways and Wounds	120
XVI	No News Is Awful	124
XVII	Spring Cleaning	128
XVIII	A String that Stretches	135
XIX	Trails and Tails	148
XX	More About Mo	154
XXI	Which Way Is North?	160
XXII	Lesson from a Dragonfly	167
XXIII	A Believe-It-or-Not Day	177
XXIV	Whatzit?	189
XXV	"Urch"	202
XXVI	Lieutenant in a Kimono	212
XXVII	A Super-Nut with Whiskers	225
XXVIII	Carry On!	230

I

EENY, MEENY, MINEY, MO—

DUKE had stood for a long time looking out the wide windows of our little north-woods cabin. A springtime tempest was raging through the surrounding forest, setting the growing things to bowing frantically as though royalty were passing by. Our small woodland lake, generally so quiet and gentle, was whipped into a foam. The waters raced past our island animated by wild enthusiasm as if they had found a short cut to the sea.

Duke's eyes danced and sparkled with merriment as he watched this spectacle of wilderness power and abandon. There was a stern but pleasant challenge to it that he loved. Intermittently he would emit a little parcel of laughter. While more musical, these laughs were not unlike the chatter of a kingfisher. And like the ever-ready twitter of that strange bird, one knew that Duke had plenty more laughs where those came from.

Duke was a wonderful laugher! He was so filled with natural good humor he could get a giggle out of almost any situation. All the world loves a laugher! When anyone is so constituted that he watches for the merry side of things, everyone and everything wants to present him with the joke, jest or prank which will provoke a *cackle spasm*—as we termed Duke's joyous outbursts. Whenever we heard a funny story, we wanted to tell it or write it to Duke. If we saw something ludicrous in nature, we simply had to share it with him. Always we knew what to expect. He would stand listening with arms folded, a little habit that made his powerful broad shoulders look mountainous. From his height of six feet two inches he would look down at the speaker, his eyes a-twinkle with anticipation and his lips practicing little smiles. As the story, joke or gag unfolded, his attention was so rapt it helped you say your piece. Little samples of Duke's laugh would come bubbling out as if he just couldn't hold it all and some was spilling.

You never had to say, "It's time to laugh, Duke." He was always 'way ahead of you, courtesy alone making him restrain himself until you had finished. But when the point of the story had been reached he would bend over, slipping his folded arms to his stomach as if a pain had suddenly developed there. He would lift one leg, balancing on the other, looking like a great blue heron about to take off. All this was but the recoil. We storytellers would stand back and watch—it was what we had been bargaining for.

Duke would unwind and burst into a cackle spasm that would nearly set the furniture to dancing. He would beat his broad chest and hold his hands to his sides while he giggled one cadenza after another. Then he would begin adding to the original joke certain little embellishments of his own that prolonged and spread the epidemic of merriment. We used to say, "You've never heard your own story until you tell it to Duke." Everything funny was funnier when shared with him.

Nature seemed to have discovered this fact that May morning. Usually there is very little that is funny about a near hurricane such as thrashed about us. But because Duke was looking out from our window, the forest was behaving like a convention of comedians. It was one of those days when gray clouds raced in unbroken array at treetop level, driven by a fitful and erratic northwest wind. Powerful pines bent condescendingly in the gale, which teased at the coiffures of birches and elms. Little itinerant showers trailed across the rugged north country, looking like torn veils half discarded by the clouds.

The scene doesn't sound humorous in description, but to Duke it presented an endless comedy. On the ground near the cabin some grain and crumbs of bread had been placed for our little friends of the forest. Two chipmunks coming from opposite directions, frantic to get at this food, had collided head-on. There was a fierce scramble for a moment, marked by indignant squeals and squeaks. Then the two diminutive creatures raced away in opposite directions to perch on stumps, there to sit with partially restrained tempers telling each other what a chipmunk thinks of a chipmunk who bumps into him. Duke had watched every detail of this incident with keen discernment. He saw things in it that few would, and maybe some things that were not there; but what he saw plus what he thought carried him away anew on the wings of mirth. He humanized those chipmunk reactions, read the meaning of their expressions, and interpreted their speech until he had patched up a story worthy of Mark Twain.

Event followed fast on event in nature's vaudeville that morning. This technique of overlapping acts is often used in the theater. Entertainers say the second laugh should be started in an audience before the first has fully subsided. This seemed to be what nature had in mind. But assuredly the whole show was most disconcerting to my wife Giny and to me. Giny was in the kitchen creating culinary masterpieces in the form of pumpkin pies, or at least she was trying to. But she thought more of Duke and his perpetual circus than she did of mixing dough and making the filling. For my part, there was a perfectly blank piece of paper in my typewriter, waiting patiently for writings long overdue at the publishers'. My fingers toyed with the typewriter keys, and occasionally I would experience a flicker of an idea as to what I should write. But before I struck the first letter something new would happen in Duke's comedy, and my thoughts would go racing there.

Now a dozen proud, strutting, squawking bronzed grackles sailed in and lighted at the feeding station.

"Of all the snooty outfits I ever saw!" exclaimed Duke. "Look! They have to squeeze their squeaks out of them."

It was even so. The big black birds with funny long beaks and yellow eyes walked about with noses in the air as if in effort to snub one another and everything else as well. As they gave their harsh unmusical cries they puffed up like toy balloons, and their thin voices sounded like rusty hinges that would rather not be used. Duke said they walked like top sergeants. Their strides were disproportionately long, as if they were trying to stress their importance. A gentle tap on the windowpane put them to sudden flight. They darted through the foliage in marvelous manner, using their long tails like rudders. But in a moment they were back, searching eagerly about the feeding station for the bites of food they preferred. Obviously bread was in much favor, as they seized this first. But several who had taken pieces of crust found it still a bit too hard to suit their tastes. Hence, they took it in their beaks and flew to the bird bath, there to *ge-dunk* it deliberately! They sat patiently at one side until the bread was thoroughly soaked, and then ate it with many a squeaky cry about how good it was.

Suddenly there was a flurry of wings as the black birds were startled by some disturbance in the brush. They perched at safe height in near-by trees until they made sure what it was. Then, discovering that it offered them no harm, they returned to their eating, taking no further notice of the creature which was approaching. Down the little path that circles among young balsam trees came a funny little animal, built so close to the ground it was difficult to see its legs.

"Here comes something that looks like a cross between a dachshund and a jelly roll!" exclaimed Duke.

Giny left her dough mixing, and I left my typewriter

to see Link, our half-friendly woodchuck, approach the feeding station. Link was an odd-appearing animal. She had come out of hibernation but a short time before and her skin hung in loose folds as if she were wearing a coat much oversized. Her legs were so short it was a question whether she walked or crawled. The grackles, sensing no fear of this vegetable-eating animal, would hardly get out of her way.

Link's supreme touch of comedy was the manner in which she ate. She found pieces of bread and worked industriously at putting them away. In fact, it seemed that she worked much harder at her eating than was necessary. She sat upright like a prairie dog, holding a piece of bread in her front feet. When she was taking a bite, her lower jaw dropped so low Duke expressed

fear that it might fall off. Then as she brought it up, it would almost disappear into her pouchy cheeks and upper jaw. She looked like some aged grandmaw who had misplaced her teeth just before dinner, but with the pardonable persistence of her years just ate anyway.

There seemed to be danger that she might bite the end of her own nose.

Link got her name through no choice of her own. Her mother, a loved pet of ours, had been called Sausage because she was ground hog. Link was a little member of the Sausage family, hence Link Sausage, or just plain Link. Terrible puns, I know, but the woodchucks didn't mind.

Two more natural-born comedians appeared on the scene—Salt and Pepper, our pesky pet porcupines. They came waddling out of the brush, one behind the other, walking with slow, measured stride. The grackles and Link did not so much as glance their way. For no creature has anything to fear of the old porcupine—so long as he does not attack the quill-pig. Normally porcupines do not eat meat, and so are not interested in destroying the creatures with whom they share the woods.

I have often wished I could find a way to describe the porcupine. There seems to be nothing with which to compare him. The porky isn't like anything but himself. He is slowness personified—slow living, slow moving, slow eating, slow thinking.

Salt and Pepper that stormy day walked along as though they were going no place and had eternity to make it in. We did not see them often, and very seldom found them together. In their baby days they had lived on our island. But the wide world had claimed them. They went where they wished when they pleased. Occasionally they would return to the island, generally singly, but once in a while they came together. Always on their visits they acted as if they had never been away, walking in as they did now, as if saying, "Hi, folks, is dinner ready?" They were so bowlegged they almost stepped on their own feet. The great mass of quills which covered their backs swayed from side to side like a load of hay as they moved along at turtle pace. Their noses dipped so low they almost scraped the ground, and their tails dragged along. Our experience has taught us that they have a very definite destination in mind, and head directly for a chosen somewhere. But to watch them gives the impression that they don't care where they go, when they arrive or how soon they come back.

Salt and Pepper nosed through the flock of squeaking grackles, then nearly bumped into Link. Reluctantly she moved a few inches to one side to let them pass. They investigated the cracked corn on the ground, and found it not to their liking. Bits of bread, too, failed to satisfy. We could hear their voices even above the howl of the wind, and we knew full well what these calls meant. All guests at the feeding station had to be disturbed because those two spoiled brats not only were choosy about their food, but were fussy about the form it was in. Bread was what they wanted, but not crumbs. They wanted whole slices! We tossed some out to them, causing grackles to dash into tall trees, and Link to scurry under the house. Then the pampered old porkies waddled over to the bread slices, and each picked up one. Braced by their strong and useful tails, they sat back comfortably, held their food in their front feet, and looked somewhat like little monkeys.

Now each began to eat in strictly individual style. Salt rammed his blunt and homely nose right into the center of his chosen slice of bread, gnawing and nibbling until he had made a round hole. When he reached the crust, he dropped that piece and picked up another. Pepper, on the other hand, began eating her slice from the side, chewing her way right through. Then she dropped the two remaining pieces and selected another whole slice. Grackles and Link had now returned, and they picked up the bits left by the wasteful and extravagant porkies. On the whole not a crumb was lost, but it was not through any virtue of those porcupines.

Each moment now the number of wild-folk guests at the feeding station increased. Eight red-winged black birds circled in and lighted in spite of the mild objection of the grackles. We had been two years gaining the friendship of these redwings. As a rule, they are not very friendly birds. But one, in his first year's plumage, had broken tradition and come to our cabin. Apparently his coming convinced others that we were to be trusted, for now there were a number of these beautiful birds visiting us regularly. As they flew in, it seemed they were sending semaphore signals by the flashing of the red spots on their wings.

At the supreme moment of this woodland banquet, we took count of our guests. It was startling. On the ground at one time, within a space of a hundred square feet,

there were eleven grackles, eight redwings, two song
sparrows, five juncoes, two robins, one nuthatch, six chipmunks, one woodchuck and two porcupines!

A bit later all these creatures had left as if to set the
stage for the next event. Now Blooey, our friendly blue
jay, put on an act. When a strong wind blows, birds
face into it on landing, perching or taking off. It is a
fundamental technique which all airmen must know. No
doubt our big old blue jay had this in mind as he came
gliding into the feeding area. He floated in wearing his
typical cocksure expression, apparently proud of his
prowess on wing, and in right humor for a few tasty
nibbles. But as he reached the ground the wind whipped
around the cabin and came up behind him. It caught
Blooey's beautiful tail, and without regard for his feelings or his reputation as a flier, unceremoniously tipped
him over, laying him for a brief moment flat on his back
in a little puddle of rain water. With a wild flurry of
feathers and wings he was up instantly, not hurt in the
least—but horribly mortified! In uncontrolled anger he
gave one of those sharp blue-jay cries with such emphasis
that his voice broke into a nondescript sound like a teen-
age youth blasting two tones at once. Then Blooey flew
away, screaming wildly, too much embarrassed and upset
to indulge in even a bite.

I felt actually concerned about Duke as he saw this.
He bent over convulsed, but no sound would come out.
His attempt at a laugh was just all breath. He went into
his blue-heron pose, his arms all wrapped around an ache

somewhere in his midsection. I was grateful when I saw him draw in breath, for I had been fearful lest this intake would come too late. His face was red and tears were peering out of his eyes to find an easy course down his cheeks. After several desperate efforts he managed to get through a few little weak giggles, and finally he was pouring forth "Haw! Haws!" all over the cabin.

"What is it now?" asked Giny, coming hurriedly in from the kitchen.

I rose from my typewriter to get my share of the joke, whatever it was.

But Duke had no breath for words at that moment. He could only point out the window. We tried to control our own laughter and get the story out of him, but there is nothing more infectious than laughter—heaven be praised! Duke made effort to tell us. He would swallow, wipe tears from his eyes, point out the window, explosively utter the one word "Blooey——!" and then lose himself in another unrestrained outburst.

As we coaxed and coaxed for the story, he tried to explain it to us in pantomime. Flapping his long muscular arms like wings, he imitated Blooey coming in to the feeding station. He flew about the cabin, much to its discomfiture. He aped the long, gliding flight of the bird, his arms held rigid and straight from his shoulders. Suddenly he swooped low, as Blooey had before the puddle, and then he turned a complete somersault. Rising and rubbing the sore places, he looked up with an expression of extreme embarrassment. Then he gave a much exaggerated imitation of Blooey's two-tone cry, and went flying at double time out the door to the kitchen.

By this time the three of us had cackle spasms. It was many minutes before we had attained a mood sufficiently calm to gain the story of the old blue jay and his calamity.

Giny and I were treasuring every merry moment with Duke. He had been at our Sanctuary often before, and always his coming was a happy event. But there was special significance in this visit. He looked the same as we had always known him, dressed in his faded woolen shirt and wrinkled khaki trousers. But we were mindful that in the cabin clothes closet hung a uniform of the United States Army, cut to fit his fine athletic figure. On the shoulders of the jacket were pinned the twin bars— "railroad tracks," he called them—of the rank of captain. Duke had worked hard through long tedious months of training to gain that rank. These few days with us were part of his final leave before he left for some distant and unannounced battle zone. His parents, in a near-by city, had insisted that he come, even though it took a few precious days from his time with them. They knew well what it meant to him. There were difficult experiences before our captain. The laughter, beauty and solitude he was taking into his heart might be the last he would know for a long time.

A single glance at him would tell anyone why he was called Duke. He certainly suggested nobility. While he had always been strong and active, his army training had marshaled his strength and put it at his finger tips. He stood straight as a red pine, and looked as sturdy. He was lithe and graceful as a cat. His naturally curly hair had twisted tighter under the southern sun at training camp, and his skin was bronze as an Indian's. As he stood before the cabin window that morning, he was the personification of strong, capable, cheerful, fearless American manhood.

Now Duke had found a new amusing incident out in the gray day.

"What is it *this* time?" asked Giny, who had at last slipped the pies into the oven. I pulled the still blank sheet of paper from my typewriter and got to my feet. We joined Duke to watch an outboard motorboat which had just come around a point of land and was slicing its way through companies of marching waves. Sometimes the craft seemed to leap free of the water as it literally skipped from the crest of one wave to the next. Quick-fading flowers of spreading spray marked its rough course through the waters. Duke wished he might be out there. Certainly that boat was the center of an exciting adventure. The lone occupant had a mammoth playground all to himself, and he was making the most of it.

"He's heading this way!" exclaimed Duke.

The boat had altered its course and was coming directly toward us, bouncing, leaping over those endless moving, liquid hurdles. It slowed down in the relatively calm water at the lee side of our island, and rounded a point to the little bay where our boathouse stands.

Duke and I donned raincoats and went to meet our caller. It proved to be a neighbor boy, Bill, who had defied the gale to bring us an odd little gift.

"Merry Christmas!" Bill said, as he handed us a small brown basket. It was packed with layers of cotton, and obviously contained something delicate and precious, for our young neighbor handled it with great tenderness and care. Duke took the gift half singing his comment, "I have a hunch there's trouble in here!"

Together we put the layers of cotton aside, amid repeated warnings from our visitor to "be careful, now." Presently we looked on the gift itself. First we gave little gasps of surprise and admiration, and then we began call ing in unison: "Giny! Oh, Giny! Oh, Gine-e-e-e-e!"

"I'm afraid the pies will burn if I come," she called from the cabin. "What is it?"

"Let them burn!" we called back. "You just have to see this present."

Giny threw a raincoat over her head and came running to the boathouse, to join us in our *ohs* and *ahs*.

In the center of the soft, warm nest lay four tiny baby red squirrels, or chickarees, not more than three weeks old. There were hardly enough of them to make one good mouse! But their tiny eyes were open, and they looked at us with babylike innocence and fearlessness. Giny began mothering them at once. She straightened out their tiny little feet, stroked their rich red fur with her finger tips and adjusted the cotton covering so that only their heads were exposed.

A shower of questions was hurled at Bill. Where had he found them? Where were their parents? When had they been fed?

Gradually we got the story. These little chickarees had lived in the hollow of a tree near his cabin. Our neighbors had been watching them, had heard their baby cries and had noted the mother squirrel coming and going. Then hours passed and she did not come to her family. The hunger cries of the little ones became desperate and incessant. As the neighbors hesitated, uncertain what they should do, the tiny squirrels took matters in their own hands. Out of the nest they came, half crawling, half falling down the side of the tree to the ground. This food business was a serious matter! And they were going to find some, somewhere!

"We picked them up," our young visitor explained. "They were not the least bit afraid. We fed them diluted milk with an eye dropper. Boy, how they went after it! I thought we would never get them filled. There were five of them at first, but one ran under the house. We couldn't catch him to give him his dinner."

"Poor little fellow!" said Giny. "Perhaps you will get him later. Why, the creatures are hungry now. Look at this!"

She had touched the nose of one of them with her little finger, and he tried desperately to nurse on it. That was hint enough for Giny. Away she went to warm some milk and round up some eye droppers. Duke, Bill and I endeavored to warm the squirming squirrelets with the palms of our hands, telling them a thousand foolish things they didn't understand.

When the food was ready, Duke was the first to feed our new little charges. Later we often spoke of that impressive scene. There were qualities that touched our hearts as well as our hopes. The hair-trigger sense of humor was silenced for the moment, and we looked on another side of this young captain's nature—his strong gentleness, kindliness and tenderness shown in the care of helpless creatures.

Here he was, fresh from schooling in the savage arts of war, trained to combat an enemy who would if possible drive civilization and decency from human experience. Contrary to his natural inclinations, Duke had learned all the up-to-date tricks of viciousness, and he had strength to carry them out. Many times he had startled us with his agility. We had watched him climb trees with a speed and ease that might have been envied by a monkey. We saw him climb a rope hand over hand to a limb twenty feet from the ground, and jump down lightly. Unpretentiously he demonstrated how to disarm a man of a gun or knife, and how to defend himself if attacked from behind. While he was gentle with his demonstrations, I, as the victim, was glad no seriousness was involved.

But strong as he was, no angel of mercy could have shown greater tenderness than he with those helpless and dependent little animals. This experience came to him as an opportunity to be himself for a moment, to indulge the incomparable joy of being kind.

"Now come on, you fellows!" Duke was saying to the baby squirrels. He pulled back layers of cotton, revealing again the little huddle of tiny creatures. "Come on. Who's first? Eeny, Meeny, Miney, Mo——"

But Eeny crawled under Meeny, and Miney crawled over Eeny, and Mo crawled under the three of them. They kept crawling one under the other and squirming about until Duke said they looked like a mass of fur-covered fishworms. Without waiting to complete his count, he picked up one of them and brought him out for dinner. The tiny thing was badly frightened and struggled to be free. But he ceased his struggles and his eyes closed in contentment as the eye dropper came into play and he tasted the first swallow of warm milk. With quick realization that he was in the hands of a friend, he took hold of the dropper with his little front feet. Not until he had been fed six droppers full was he satisfied. Then he was placed back in his cotton-filled nest and sought a corner where he could indulge in a comfortable carefree nap.

Eeny was now fed and contented. Captain Duke carried on his nursing duties. With hands trained to Ranger tactics, he fed Meeny, Miney and Mo until they were as wide as they were long. The four, now duly named and nourished, were tucked away in their bed, where they dropped off into squirrel dreamland, lullabyed by the final finger caresses and soft words of our soldier.

Bill now took his leave with the promise that if he found the fifth squirrel he would bring him at once.

As he started his motor it made a roar that was startling—but not as startling as Giny's shriek that came at the same moment! Duke and I whirled around to see her racing off toward the cabin.

"What is it?" we cried, running after her.

"The pies! The pies!" she cried. "I can smell them!"

I brought the bad news to Duke, who had returned to the basket of squirrels, feeling more concern about them than he did about the burning bakery. The pies were black as cinders, and the oven had enough deposit on it to account for a half day of scrubbing.

"I always liked canned peaches anyway," said Duke.

II

—AND STILL-MO!

ALL through the night and into the next day the north-west gale blew with undiminished fury. Our weather report was from observation, for there was not an hour passed but that someone was awake and up—seeing if Eeny, Meeny, Miney and Mo were all right.

We had brought them, basket and all, into the cabin and placed them before the fireplace. Duke fed them until they couldn't wiggle. Giny tucked them snugly in their bed of cotton, and we put such a stack of wood on the fire that the only way another piece could have been added was to drop it through the chimney. Then we went to bed. However, it wasn't more than a half-hour later when I heard Duke come in from the tent house where he loved to sleep. He tiptoed to the fireplace, and I heard him chuckle softly as he moved the basket farther away from the lively flames.

"You might as well laugh out loud, Duke. We're wide awake," I called.

Duke did. "I was afraid these little guys would be too warm," he explained, "so I sneaked in to see. Do you suppose I ought to feed them again while I'm up?"

"Good heavens, no! You couldn't get more milk in them unless you forced it in with a tire pump!"

"OK," said Duke, a little disappointed, "but one of 'em is looking at me as if he wanted something."

"He probably wants to be let alone so he can get some sleep."

"All right—guess I can take a hint!" Mingling a laugh with baby talk, Duke tucked the squirrel tots away again and placed the basket where he thought it should be. When he had gone to his tent, Giny went in to see how well his tucking had been done, and she moved the basket still farther away from the fire. A little later when the flames had died down, I went out and moved it closer. Duke came in with some wood a few minutes after that and built up the fire. Next Giny went out and moved the basket away. Then I moved it up. Then Duke moved it back. It went up and back, up and back, until those poor little things must have felt seasick. Three times during the night the captain warmed some milk and fed them. Just as the gray clouds were showing the first faint light of dawn, he tried it a fourth time. Giny and I had dropped off to sleep for a few minutes, and we were awakened by Duke's knock on our door.

"What is it, Duke?" I asked.

"The squirrels are gone!" he exclaimed. "The basket is empty!"

Now there was excitement. We dressed and joined Duke in a search that was frantic, though not long. Apparently the basket by the fire was too warm a nest for our orphans, and they had sought out places more to their liking. Two of them were curled up together back of our encyclopedias, one was huddling behind the mantel clock, and the fourth had made himself more difficult to find by hiding in the sofa. They were restored to their basket, now far from the fire, and seemed right glad to be together again.

"We aren't going to keep those tykes confined anywhere for very long," observed Duke, as we sat at the breakfast table. "Can you imagine them getting around that way? Why, one of them is hardly as large as a peanut!"

A baby chickaree matures rapidly. Not for long is he a helpless dependent infant. In his world there is every reason for growing up in a hurry. There are too many enemies that can find his nest and cause trouble. He must be able to move quickly, and learn early the tricks that give him protection.

But there were new events in the making. Giny glanced out the front windows and exclaimed excitedly, "Here comes Bill!"

"And how!" Duke's rejoinder had more meaning than is usual in that cliché. How that boat was cutting through the gray, foam-streaked waters! It leaped, reared and dipped like a bucking bronco. Sometimes it disappeared completely for an instant in the valley between two waves, only to come volplaning over the crest of the next one, slapping it as if in utter defiance. We could hear the motor snarling, and from the sound we knew that Bill had turned loose every ounce of power. It was an animated picture we looked on. Surely something had inspired even the boat itself to reach our island in the quickest possible time.

We met Bill at our boathouse. He was breathless with excitement. "I got him!" he said. "But he's a devil!"

"You got whom?"

"The other red squirrel, the fifth one. You are welcome to him. He kept us awake all night."

Number Five was a problem! He had more pep and impishness than all the other four combined. Our neighbors had caught him about dusk the night before, when the little fellow had come back to his nest. They had held him and fed him, but he did not welcome their aid. He struggled and bit and scratched in their hands. Only sweetened warm milk calmed him down, and that was just for a moment.

"He isn't bigger than a beetle," declared Bill, looking at us with sleepy eyes, "but he was all over the place in nothing flat. He went over and under the furniture, climbed the curtains, jumped up in the cupboard, plowed into the sugar bowl, and tipped over everything. We put him in a cardboard box. He chewed his way out of it. We put him in a tin can. He made so much fuss we had to take him out. The only place he would spend the night was in a breadbox filled with a blanket."

Number Five had made his water journey confined in a stationery box. But he banged against the lid until it looked as if there were an internal earthquake.

"He's all yours!" Bill handed the box over with obvious relief. "Take him, and may God give you strength!"

Bill went home at high speed to take a nap, while Giny, Duke and I took the rollicking Number Five to meet his brothers.

"What do you call squirrel quintuplets?" I asked Duke.

"*Squints,* I suppose."

"*Squints* it is!"

Number Five recognized his relatives, but he was surely a bad influence on them. He plowed right into them, once he had been dumped into their basket. He bit one on the tail, a second on the ear, and scratched and mauled the others until he had them all in the same impish humor he was in. They fought, twisted and tumbled until the basket bounced about like an enlarged Mexican jumping bean.

Number Five looked self-sufficient and almost mean. His expression seemed to say to us, "I can take care of myself. Just let me alone!" He hopped out of the basket, only to be caught and carried back in Duke's large cupped hands. Far from being appreciative of this attention, he bit Duke's fingers. His baby teeth were not very effective, but sharp enough to make Duke glad to put him down.

It was obvious that the basket would not be a suitable home for those lively youngsters for long. In fact, with the coming of Number Five, it was already inadequate. Out near Duke's tent house stood a large wire cage that had served as the home of many animals through the years. Rack and Ruin the raccoons had used it for a few days; so had Salt and Pepper our pet porcupines, and bear cubs, beavers, birds and tiny deer, all under our protection until they grew out of the baby stage. Hastily we prepared this for the Squints. We filled it with newly cut brush, covered the floor with moss and logs, placed a cloth-filled wooden box in one corner as a nest. Then we draped a heavy canvas over it to break the wind.

By midmorning the new accommodations were ready for the Squints. It was none too soon. They were simply boiling out of that basket. Giny had spent half her time retrieving them from various nooks and corners. Number Five had climbed up on a curtain rod and refused to come down. Only Duke could reach him, and he was bitten again for his trouble.

There were a few minutes of calm while they were fed, after which they all went to sleep in a huddle in the basket. We seized on this opportunity to make final preparations for placing the little orphans in their new home.

Water and various kinds of food—peanuts, bread and corn meal—were provided in outlandish proportions, for Duke had charge of this. We inspected the cage for any breaks in the wire. Then we assembled five colors of paint. This was not only to be a transplanting operation for the squirrels, it was to be a christening. Each one must have identity, and be marked in such a way that we would recognize him.

Giny brought the basket to the cage, and with great solemnity we began the ceremony. I uncovered the little rascals and reached for one of them, whereupon Number Five squealed defiantly and burrowed his way to the bottom of the heap.

I lifted one, and touching him between the front shoulders with a small brush dipped in green paint, I said: "I dub thee *Eeny!*"

With the aid of black paint, the next was christened *Meeny.* White paint designated *Miney,* and brown was for *Mo.*

"And the-e-e-e-e I du-u-u-u-u-b——" I dragged out my ceremony while trying to catch the rampant Number Five. He squealed invectives entirely too severe for his age, and crawled wildly among rolls of cotton. When my hand caught up with him, he bit my finger.

"Come out here, you little angel," I insisted. "You are going to be christened if I have to put you in irons. And red paint it shall be, for where you are there is danger."

"But what are you going to call him?" asked Duke

"You have Eeny, Meeny, Miney and Mo—but who is he?"

I was ready for this. Raising the squirming scamp high, I touched him with red paint, saying in tremulous voice, "And thee I dub—*Still-Mo!*"

Duke went into a cackle spasm.

III

BAD DREAM AHEAD

IN THE days that immediately followed the coming of
the Squints we had no difficulty finding Captain Duke.
He spent most of his time sitting in a corner of the squirrels' cage playing with the funny little creatures. They
accepted him as a part of their lives, and with absolute
freedom ran all over him as if he were a tree. They
perched on his head. They ran in and out of his trouser
legs. They disappeared down the collar of his shirt and
came out his sleeves. And not infrequently they went to
sleep in his pockets. Often when we called him to lunch
or dinner he would shout back some such message as
"Can't come now, I'm a dormitory for these young redskins." He had rather miss a meal than move and disturb
them.

Duke had a wonderful time watching and studying the
simple little animals. He forgot completely his spick-
and-span uniform bearing the captain's insignia. For
him this was a leave indeed—his thought fully absorbed
with the natural and real things of the world. The
war, as purely a human invention as the implements of
destruction employed in it, was far removed from this
realm of plants and creatures, tides and seasons, all aris-

ing from a principle and power beyond human compre-
hension.

We were careful not to recall the military thought to
him. Only once did he speak of it, and then briefly. One
evening we stood looking at Venus, the evening star,
shining resplendently in the afterglow. The world had
come to rest. The Squints were huddled in a furry red
ball in one corner of their nest within the cage. Up
toward the stars in the foliage of a white birch a robin
uttered his sleepy song. Duke was silent and serious, his
infectious good humor tucked away while his mind dwelt
on deeper things.

"And this *is* the world of reality!" he said quietly, as
though thinking aloud. "The world that was, and is, and
always will be!"

He paused for a moment, and Giny and I made no
reply. In the distance a barred owl deepened the silence
with its weird cry.

"How it lifts hope to know that this world of nature
pays no attention to human bluff and blunder!" Duke
continued. "It just goes on blooming, growing and unfolding. We can destroy some of its effects, but none of
its causes. We can burn a forest, but we cannot prevent
a new one from coming."

He paused again, and we stood in silence. It was one
of those sacred moments when thought is realizing great
truths, and one must be careful not to break the spell. It
took a few more minutes of starlight and solitude to
bring forth Duke's next words.

"After the First World War," Duke began again, "someone asked General Pershing what was the most wonderful thing he saw in France. He replied that it was the way the larks sang during battles."

Duke stopped. We feared he had turned to a subject that would disquiet thought, but he knew well the ground on which he stood.

"I hold to that!" the young soldier said. "I know what is ahead. The kind of training we have received tells us what to expect. But it helps to know that we cannot lose this." He looked about at the nocturnal beauty. "It will be here when we return, and birds will sing even on the battlefields."

Giny slyly wiped away a tear, and I swallowed hard a lump in my throat that wouldn't go down. But Duke laughed a little. He would laugh whenever it would help matters.

"It seems to me like going into a dream voluntarily," he went on. "It is a different kind of a dream. Most dreams just happen to you. But this dream we choose, and we deliberately walk right into it. I dread it, and frankly I am afraid—but I wouldn't miss it for the world. Because it is *our* dream, and we must see it through. It is a bad dream, like the kind we have in sleep when we have eaten something indigestible. Well, we have thought something that is indigestible, we human beings have. We have been feasting on selfishness and hate. No wonder such a nightmare has been conjured up. But since I have been here where the real world just keeps rolling on, I know that all this other *is* just a kind of dream. And when it is over and we all awake again—*this* will be just as it is now. There will be robins singing, stars sparkling, trees growing, solitude and peace still in the world—yes, and baby red squirrels, too!"

That little speech presented the true character of our soldier. Everyone is a philosopher, for everyone must have his notion of life and duty. Duke had formed his. The great tragedy of human experience—*war*—was to him a dream taking place in ignorance and evil thinking. He would not flatter it by calling it real. While toying with the tiny squirrels so lightheartedly, he had been finishing his conviction. This changing but unchangeable, ever different, ever the same world of nature was his parable. For here were things that last, things that are true, things that antedate and outlast human mistakes and misery.

"And I believe I know what real peace would be," Duke continued, as we walked toward the cabin. "It doesn't make peace just to stop fighting, though it helps. And there is more to it than just being here where it is quiet and beautiful, though that helps too. Once in a while I have reached the place where peace was so close at hand that I knew where to seek it at least. It is when I forget myself, and as someone said, 'look through nature to nature's God.' "

We had paused for a moment where a little break in the trees let us look toward the northern horizon. Northern lights were glowing about the North Star. Several meteors streaked the heavens as we watched.

"Yes." Duke picked up his thought. "You don't really find peace until you get close to *Him*—some way, somehow—I wish I knew."

IV

TO MAKE A LONG TAIL SHORT

THE paint spots which had been placed on the Squints for identification purposes faded and disappeared rather soon. But they lasted long enough to let us learn the characteristics of each squirrel so that we could know one from the other. You do not identify animals just by some aspect any more than you do people. It is the whole being of the creature that you recognize. You know the way he walks, moves, calls, and what he is most apt to do. You learn his likes and dislikes, his disposition, his habits—in fact, you know him so well you recognize him without knowing just how you do it.

Before Duke's leave had ended, he knew Eeny, Meeny, Miney, Mo and Still-Mo so well he could identify them in the dark. At least he claimed he could. When we asked for proof, he resorted to paraphrasing an old gag:

"Well," he said, "in the dark I put my finger in Eeny's mouth, and if Miney bites me, it is Still-Mo. On the other hand, if Meeny nestles up to my hand it is Eeeny, unless Still-Mo doesn't do anything—then I know it is Mo."

We couldn't argue with that, for we wouldn't know where to begin.

Duke kept a diary of the Squints as long as he was there. He recorded how rapidly they grew, and how their instincts and natural ways of living began to appear. The little fellows obviously knew they were squirrels, and were right proud of the fact. With amazing ability they climbed about the small trees and branches that had been placed in their cage. They gathered little bits of bark and leaves from the floor to make play nests of their own in selected spots. To sharpen their teeth and strengthen their jaws, they chewed on twigs and branches. They chattered after the manner of their kind, sounding like a boy giving a vocal imitation of a machine gun. Within a week they had taken themselves off their milk diet. It was infantile food and might be all right for youngsters, but they were now over a month old and they would have no more of it! Instead, they chewed viciously at peanuts and bread crusts, and took well to the buds, grasses, cabbage and carrots we gave them. Immediately they began storing food, squirrel-fashion, hiding it in corners and crotches and under leaves.

Duke sat in the cage quietly for a long time one day, and then broke into a cackle spasm. Giny and I went running to find out what the latest joke was. The chickarees had kept Duke giggling much of the time. Now we found him running his fingers through his long curly hair, searching for peanuts, laughing the while. Still-Mo, it seemed, had decided that would be a mighty fine place to store some food for the future. So while Duke had held perfectly still watching the operation, the saucy squirrel made trip after trip from his head to the pan of food and back, each time bringing a nut and concealing it among the curls.

"I held still," said Duke, "until the rascal began bringing bread crumbs and pine cones, and then I decided he had gone far enough."

He combed nine peanuts out of his hair, while Still-Mo crouched in a corner and chattered his disapproval.

As with all animals, these five little fellows were strictly individual. Duke was a good observer, and his diary of the Squints recorded traits that we could recognize as long as they remained under our observation.

Eeny, who wore the green paint, was the gentle one, the natural pet, the lamb. She was the only female of the family but certainly no weakling. In childish squabbles with her four brothers she held her own, and they respected her. But she was always the approachable one. When Duke crawled into the cage, it was Eeny who first came to him. If the morning were cool, she might work her way into a pocket, lie contentedly in his big cupped hands, or nestle up to his neck.

Red squirrels by nature are wary creatures and avoid intimate friendships with human beings. Eeny came close to breaking this rule. Even when the day came for the Squints to burst out of their cage and take up life in the woods, this little one was hesitant. Continually she reached back to us, and sometimes acted as if she wished we would learn to climb trees and live on a woods diet so we could be together more. Many of her little baby friendly habits with us were continued until she was a veteran forest squirrel.

Eeny's expression was mild and affectionate. That is not always true of her kind. A red squirrel lives in a belligerent world, and likes it. He banters and argues with all the creatures about him, asks no favors, and gives none. Hence he looks saucy, and is. But Eeny wore a somewhat kindly expression. Her sharp little eyes would look at us with lively interest written in them, but no hostility. Sometimes when Duke was stroking the little creature, though her back was hardly large enough to give one good rub, she would close her eyes in obvious contentment.

Unquestionably Eeny was Duke's favorite. "This is my pal," our captain would say as he reached down to pick up half a handful of the little creature. "She and I have lots of secrets. We know all the answers, don't we, old top?" And tiny little "old top" winked as if she agreed with all that had been said.

Meeny was appropriately named. No girl-teasing, hair-pulling, spitball-shooting, teacher-baiting grammar-school boy ever thought up more meanness than he. He wore the black paint, but not for long. He figured out how to scratch or rub it off on the wires of his cage. Surely he was a smart little scamp, along with his deviltry. He was the first one to figure out the various problems Duke continually gave the youngsters. It was Meeny who first learned that Duke carried peanuts in various pockets, and he mastered the art of getting them. But he never misrepresented his motive. He went into those pockets for the sole purpose of obtaining food, and there was no pretense at making it a friendly gesture. Eeny would enter a pocket anyway, liked to stay there, and would welcome the hand that reached in to her. Not so with Meeny. If there was no food, there was no reason to be there. Out he would come and tell Duke a few things in saucy squirrel talk. His disposition showed in every move. He was seldom still, even for a moment. Always he acted like a runner toeing the mark while he waits for the starter's gun. His tail frisked about and his head jerked, and he snapped out little chirps right and left as he stood always on a tension. Duke had many a laugh about Meeny.

"I know people like him," he said. "They live on edge as if the whole world were just waiting to take a bite at them, always try to outsmart someone, and are hardly willing to come close enough to shake hands. They seem to have the notion that everyone is trying to do them out of something and they want to do others first. They just bring trouble on themselves, for you can't trust a fellow who won't trust you."

One day I heard Duke talking to Meeny in a most confidential way. It was futile, of course, for Meeny had not the slightest notion what all that wordy sound meant. But the conversatior was worth while, for Duke was clearing up his own thoughts. Maybe that is one of the greatest benefits of animal friends. They help us think things out.

"Meeny," Duke was saying in tones patient and kindly, "you're just smart enough that you ought to be a little bit smarter."

Meeny was perched on the top of the nest house in the cage looking right at Duke with anything but a friendly attitude. His little feet gripped the boards tensely, his tail circled over his back, and he made small nervous steps constantly as if practicing his getaway.

"Take it easy," Duke went on. "No one is going to hurt you or take anything from you. If you were as smart as you think you are, you would know that. A fellow doesn't know very much as long as he thinks the world is all against him—because it isn't true. But don't you understand we can't be kind to you unless you will let us? You don't take in the goodness that is all around you. You're fighting with your own funny ideas all the time. You cause the very things you are afraid of. Come on now, relax! The rest of us are not as bad as you think we are! Give us a chance to be nice to you. Here . . . here's a peanut just to prove I mean it."

Meeny advanced one nervous, quick step after another toward the peanut. You would have thought he was snatching it from the very gates of Hades. When his nose touched it, he grabbed it with all the bad manners he could muster, and raced to a far corner of the cage where he indulged in a chatter that sounded like anything but gratitude or polite conversation.

"I give up," said Duke. "Meeny, you dumb cluck! I guess you'll always be that way."

Miney was a little male, but he had all the vanity that is supposed to belong to the other sex. He primped and posed and fussed at his appearance continually. "Don't ever put a mirror in there," warned Duke, "for that little guy could starve to death looking at himself." It was Miney whom we first saw when we approached the cage. He was always in some prominent spot, as if waiting to be discovered and admired. Generally he was primping. He washed his face until Duke was afraid he would wear it out. He combed out his bright red fur, and was especially particular about keeping his tail fluffy. Apparently he approved of the touch of white paint that crowned his shoulders, for he made no effort to scrape it off. Possibly he thought it was the prevailing fashion, to be endured no matter what the discomfort. Miney was not quite such a pet as Eeny, but certainly he was more approachable than Meeny. He enjoyed being petted, but immediately after he would straighten out any misplaced hairs.

Mo was exactly the opposite of Miney. The brown paint on his back became black with his rolling and crawling around. Even in that clean cage he was able to find enough dirt to smear up his face. Time and again we heard Duke break into a laugh at Mo's appearance. There was always something wrong—a black streak across his mouth, a dirty spot over one eye, his tail with no two hairs in the same direction, his feet coated with dust he found in corners. But his disposition was good, and Duke adored him.

"If you were a human being, Mo," he said, "you would probably be one of those much-loved small-town bums. You would live in a little shack all by yourself, and do little jobs around just earning enough to keep from being hungry. You would smile at everyone, and be considered a little queer. School kids would shout at you, know you by your first name, and like you. People would say you were shiftless and no good—but they would always agree that you had a heart of gold. You wouldn't take a bath often, your hair would never be combed, your clothes would be ragged, and your house disorderly. But because you didn't hate anyone, no one would hate you. A small town wouldn't be complete without at least one adorable bum, and I guess our squirrel town couldn't get along without one either."

Mo just blinked and looked up at Duke, smiling—if a squirrel can smile. Duke picked him up and put him in his pocket. Mo settled down contentedly. Duke put him on his shoulder. Mo settled there too. Anywhere was all right—it took too much energy to be fussy.

Still-Mo was the carefree, adventurous type. He owned the world, and felt that he must see it all. The red paint vanished from his shoulders within a few hours, due to his intense activity. The cage was too small for him from the day he was put in it. He explored every corner looking for a way out. He was not friendly like Eeny, but certainly not fearful like Meeny. He would run at Duke as quickly as he would run away from him. He was absolutely disrespectful to the primping Miney, and scolded Mo for his indolence. Still-Mo was like the boy who wants to put on long pants the moment he is through with the three-cornered kind; who reads Wild West novels before he learns to spell, and heads out there as soon as he can walk across a room. He looked like that. Still-Mo always gave the impression that he was just on the point of going somewhere. He did not crouch like Meeny, and there was no fear in his attitude. He stood erect but ready, his ears forward while his eyes searched for something exciting to do.

"There's a fellow in my outfit I am going to call Still-Mo," said Duke. "He was just born to be an adventurer; joined our outfit because it is the most—that is, we are the first to land. You never know where he will be or what he will do next, except that it will be OK. He won't let anything bind or restrain him. He's just a little embodied spirit of liberty. Yes sir, I am going to call him Still-Mo, Lieutenant Still-Mo—he'll get a kick out of being named after a squirrel."

Duke thought into the distance for a moment, and added with a smile and a shake of his head, *"The rascal!"*

But that little expression, said of one strong, brave man by another, told of a friendship richly deep and important.

The Squints were becoming impatient with their cage. They wanted the great big outside world they could see through the wires. We hesitated to turn them loose. There were hawks, owls, weasels and eagles out there, and a nice tender baby red squirrel would be to them like a taste of candy. But the little fellows wanted none of our coddling. Still-Mo had begun chewing futilely but determinedly at the wire. Mo was trying to burrow into the floor. Meeny and Miney were poking their little noses through the wire mesh. Even the complacent little Eeny chattered and reached for liberty.

One morning we heard Duke call to us for assistance. He had gone down to the squirrel cage. *"Jail break!"* he cried. *"Jail break!"*

We ran down and found Duke high in a cedar tree, reaching out to where Eeny was perched on a limb.

"They are all out somewhere," he called down breathlessly. "When I opened the cage to get in, they all ran out. It was a put-up job, a planned jail break. They ran in five directions. I grabbed at all of them—and didn't get one!"

By this time he had reached Eeny, who docilely permitted herself to be picked up and placed in a pocket. Duke brought her down and put her back in the cage.

The others were so active we had no trouble seeing them, but catching them was another matter. Still-Mo was climbing a white cedar. High from the ground he looked like a high-powered caterpillar. Meeny was up a white pine, and the way he raced about the branches made us shudder. Mo was poking his head out from under the cage and, of course, his face was dirty. Calling him "dirty snoot," Duke picked him up and returned him to the cage. Giny fetched a great outlay of food and placed it in the cage as a reward for coming home. It was mealtime at that, and before long we had recaptured all but Still-Mo. He was racing about the foliage in high glee, apparently trying to demonstrate to us that he was a fully grown red squirrel, quite capable of taking care of himself.

It was nearly a half-hour later when I succeeded in getting Still-Mo to come down to where I was offering him a tempting peanut. No doubt he was hungry after all his exertion, and yet he was cautious. This liberty was grand, and he did not want to lose it. A step at a time, and with many a little excited chirp, he came within my reach. While he was preoccupied with the taste of the peanut, I caught him and held him firmly in my hands. He bit me, but one must be ready to endure this occasionally in handling animals. I carried the objecting red squirrel over to the cage as Duke opened the door.

And now came an experience that I cannot even write without cringing with a peculiar sensation of pain and coating myself with goose-pimples. It isn't the kind of pain that comes of your own hurt, but rather the feeling that results when you think of hurting something or someone else you do not want to harm.

Still-Mo put up new and more successful struggles when he saw the open cage. That jail was out as far as he was concerned. He struggled, bit, scratched, squealed his indignation, and finally succeeded in filtering through my fingers. He fell to the ground, landing right beside the cage.

I grabbed wildly—and oh, I wish I hadn't! I caught hold of the very end of his tail just as he was darting under the cage. For an instant—*just* an instant—I held on. If I had let go I would have saved myself all this strange pain and these goose-pimples that haunt me as I write. Almost immediately I heard a scolding chatter near my head. There, on the side of a small hemlock tree, was Still-Mo—and I *still had his tail*—or at least half of it—*in my hand!*

A shudder went over me as I realized what had happened. There had been no struggle, no jerk; apparently Still-Mo had not fastened his clothes on very well that morning. But there was no use dodging the horrible fact —I had partly skinned him *alive!* With a groan I lifted my unwanted souvenir of skin and fur and showed it to Giny and Duke. They joined me in silent shuddering.

The least concerned of all was Still-Mo. He paid no attention to his tail, which now consisted of about two inches of fur and four inches of long, stiff, white thread-like bone. Obviously it did not hurt him much. Maybe squirrels and chipmunks are prepared to lose their tails easily. Some nature students think they are, and certainly many of the little creatures are seen with tails abbreviated. It is possible that since this part would be the first reached by pursuing enemies, they have evolved a system of giving up some of it without too severe consequences.

I am sure the whole thing hurt us more than it did Still-Mo. He went racing away, glad to pay any price for his liberty. Never again did he go into the cage. Within several days the exposed bony part of his tail had disappeared. I do not know whether he bit it off, or it dried up and broke off. Probably he got rid of it himself and forgot the entire matter. I never have forgotten it. To this day, when I think of the way he looked on that tree while I knelt there holding the freshly snatched skin in my hand, I suffer and tense up the way some people do when they hear metal scrape on glass.

This experience ended the cage stage of our Squints. Still-Mo was the martyr who had suffered and bled for the liberty of his people. We cut a squirrel-sized hole in the wire at the bottom of the cage, so that they could go and come as they pleased. Food was kept in the cage for some time, but our tiny pets had little to do with it. Their independent lives had begun.

V

GOD BE WITH YOU, DUKE!

THE morning after the jail break of the Squints, there was a different spirit in our group. It was the day of which we had said little, and which we would have delayed coming if we could. Duke's manner was changed. His face still lighted with good humor, and his conversation dealt with the usual pleasantries. But there were demanding matters at hand, and occasionally his brow wrinkled as ideas presented themselves for his attention.

"Duke, my boy," I said, walking up to his chair and laying my hand on his shoulder—sitting down he was almost as tall as I was standing—"Duke—this is it!"

"Yes," he said seriously, though he could not refrain from a little laugh, "yes, this is it. We move up today."

"Do you dread going, lad?" I asked. We had avoided talking of the time when his leave would end, and war would confront him. But it was here now, and must be faced.

"No, I mean it when I say I do not." We knew he spoke the truth. "For pleasure I would not choose the experience before me, certainly. But there is a job to be done, a job that is partly mine. I am ready now to be at it."

"And no bitterness?" I asked.

He was thoughtful for a moment. "No bitterness!" he said with conviction. "Still-Mo taught me that. He took no time to lay blame or curse his luck when misfortune came to him. It was liberty he wanted, and it was all that mattered. He could have lost the joy of liberty had he stopped to count the cost. Last night the picture was clear to me. The human race is in a cage, imprisoned by its own ignorance. All about us is a world rich in beauty and natural loveliness. Some of us can see beyond the wires of tangled thinking that hold us in. We see how happy and fine the race could be, *outside!* We have to lead in a break for this liberty. And even if some of us are hurt in the attempt, the hurts themselves may help bring freedom to all."

"I don't know just what your parable makes me," I laughed, shuddering a little as I recalled that I had pinched the tail off Still-Mo. "Yet I like it. Look out in that forest, Duke. There isn't a creature living but would rather die than surrender liberty. Freedom is a primitive instinct in nature. Something in our constitutions will never let us be contented until all men are free. We could not be satisfied otherwise even if we would. And I guess if we do leave strips of our hides behind us in our struggles, it is worth the price."

We left Duke to himself very much that day. He seemed to want to be alone with nature. He scouted the island until he had located and fed the Squints. We heard him laughing and talking to them. Chipmunks came in for attention, climbing all over him while he

donated peanuts by the handful to their insatiable appe-
tites. Salt and Pepper arrived for a romp, and Sausage
amused him with another demonstration of her chewing.
Blooey entered the scene, eying the red squirrels with
suspicion and probably conjuring up plans for making
their lives miserable.

Duke put out in a canoe and cruised along the shores.
We saw him land and disappear up a trail. An hour later
he returned and took up his canoeing again. Apparently
he was gathering thoughts into his mind to carry away
as much of this loved experience as he could.

Dinnertime came, and Duke presented himself in uniform. His boyishness was gone, and he reflected the dignity of his rank and the seriousness of his purpose. In
that dinner Giny had incorporated every favorite dish
of our soldier guest. Soon afterward it was time to go,
and we carried Duke's baggage to the boathouse.

"Just a moment," he said, holding up a finger. "Forgot
something." He ran back toward the cabin. He was gone
a few minutes, and then returned in a great hurry.

"Now let's get started. I mustn't miss that train." He
grabbed his suitcase and started to step into the boat. My
suspicions were aroused.

"No you don't, young fellow!" I said, looking at him
knowingly. "Just put that suitcase down."

"Why?" he said, trying to look innocent. "You wouldn't
want me to miss the train, would you?"

"Regardless of the train, there is nothing in the military
manual that permits an officer to do kidnaping," I said

relentlessly. "You are acting mighty suspicious, Captain, and I'd like to take a look at your pockets before you go."

There was a peculiar bulge in each side pocket of his jacket, and occasionally the bulges wiggled a little.

"OK!" he said, resignedly. "If that's the way you're going to treat me, here you are."

He reached in one pocket and drew out Mo. The little fellow looked and acted as if he wouldn't mind going along. He sat on the ground where Duke placed him, making no effort to run.

"Old dirty puss!" ejaculated Duke. "You'd never pass inspection that way, young fellow. Now," he said, turning to me, "may we go?"

"Not on your life!" I said firmly. "Come on, cough up—you have some more sins to confess."

Duke looked at me pleadingly for a moment, and then reluctantly reached into another pocket and pulled out Eeny! He took his little favorite over to a near-by tree, and after petting her a moment, placed her on a limb.

"Guess you can't go, old top," he said to the tiny squirrel. "But you wait for me now. I'm going to need you again one of these days."

I searched Duke, but he had no more squirrels. "I couldn't find the others," he said in needless explanation.

From the hour of his coming, we had been in agreement with Duke that there should be no sorrow at parting. Good-by should be said only in the original meaning of the words. Accordingly as he stepped on the train at the tiny village eleven miles from our Sanctuary, Giny and I said, "God be with you, Duke!"

"God be with you, my friends," he replied with a strong smile.

VI

WHEN THE DUMB SPEAK

Do ANIMALS know the secret of sympathy?

It has seemed to me that they do. In my childhood there was a big, homely mongrel named Sport who lived at my grandfather's farm. My summers were spent at this country home, and while old Sport lived he was the most important part of these happy adventures. Through the barefoot days that made up those vacations, old Sport and I were inseparable. He trailed behind me through the stubble fields, while I carried a stick for a gun and blazed away in imagination at desperadoes and fierce beasts. He

went with me to the old swimming hole, and guarded my
clothes while I plunged into water swarming with leeches.
Then he helped me pull off these unpleasant parasites
when I came out. He sat beside me at the table to receive
little bites I sneaked to him, and at night he curled up
on my bed, contrary to parental orders that were never
meant to be obeyed.

Then inevitably would come the worst calamity I knew
in those childish years. I would have to leave this land of
open fields, rabbits, squirrels, horses, cows, birds, and go
back to a city school. Sometimes it seemed more than I
could stand. There were tears in my heart, and in my
eyes. Old Sport never left me then. Likely he did not
understand the problem, but he knew that his friend was
unhappy and that was enough. If he could heal the hurt
by devotion and love, he wanted to do so. Wherever I
paused for a moment, he pressed against me, his ears laid
back, his eyes looking right into mine, trying to tell me
he would bite the pants off anything that bothered me if
I would just let him know what it was. If I sat down he
would crawl into my lap, whining a little in his efforts
to talk a language I could understand. Old Sport knew
the healing effect of strong sympathy. It helped much
with those childish pains to put my arms around his neck
and just feel that he cared.

In later years there was a neighbor dog named Count
who took a fancy to me. It was one of those spontaneous
friendships that cannot be wholly explained. From the
moment I saw that dog I felt an attachment to him, and

he obviously felt the same for me. During the months we
lived as neighbors, I met with the loss of a loved one.
Count took the matter of consolation on his own shoulders. He was such a little fellow, with one ear that stood
up and another that turned down. His tail was so sharply
curled it looked as if it would lift his hind feet off the
ground. He had a brown spot over one eye, and he
laughed all the time. I never saw another dog mind
other people's business as much as he did. But he knew
every mood of mine. When I was happy, he was happy.
When I was disturbed, he looked the part more than I.

I shall never forget him the hour sorrow came to me.
He found a door open and entered the house, coming to
where I sat in a chair trying to straighten out my thoughts.
Several little whines made me look down at him. Then
he came crawling on his stomach across the floor to my
feet, where he lay licking my shoes. If eyes can talk, his
spoke volumes. I reached down and lifted him to my lap.
With a desperate little whine he put his front paws on
my shoulders and laid his head against my neck. There he
stayed for half an hour, pressing against me hard as if
he were trying to get closer. I stroked his back and finally
whispered, "Count, with such love as this in the world,
no sorrow can last long!"

At one time when there were many business worries, I
had a cat that proved a most devoted creature. When
matters were bad, I formed the habit of pacing the floor
to relieve the tension. No reason for it. I guess I had seen
a picture of Napoleon doing it and thought I should do

likewise. The cat would trail right at my heels, looking up at me and calling to make me see the folly of such carryings-on. If I did not pause and pick her up, she would jump up in a chair, and from there into my arms. She would never leave me, nor stop her pleading, until I sat down and smiled. Then she would purr until she could have been heard fifty yards away.

It was most apparent to us that Salt and Pepper had taken it on themselves to cheer us up after Duke had left. While the two funny porkies had always been devoted, at this time they became extremely affectionate. Salt, who had been my particular pal, wanted to be with me constantly. He took it for granted that his attentions were welcome. If I went to my typewriter to work, he sat on the window sill outside and billed and cooed. If I stepped out the door, he came up to me at once, talking in the softest little grunts. He did not attempt to play, as at other times. Not once did he bite, scratch or raise his quills at me, as generally happened when we were both in high spirits. Whenever possible he climbed to my shoulder, where he would whisper his condolences in my ear in the quietest, most appealing voice I have ever heard a porky use.

Giny was experiencing the same attention from the two porcupines, but particularly from Pepper. This little creature, generally the more reserved of the two, insisted on being in Giny's arms much of the time. Like Salt, she dealt in soft little talk of porky poetry. What made their behavior more startling still was that for some time they had been drifting away from us. They were taking more and more to the woods. But there could be no question about it, something was influencing them. My conviction is that they definitely felt our need of sympathy and companionshp.

One seeks old friends when one's heart is heavy. The evening after Duke had left I went over a familiar trail to look for Inky, my first porcupine pet. Inky would now be about six years old, half the porcupine's usual life. His home had always been the heavy forest directly opposite our island on the mainland. The summer before I had found him fairly often. But this year he had not put in an appearance. Several times I had walked the trails at night calling for him. Only the murmur of insects answered me. There was evidence of porcupines visiting the salt lick we had prepared for Inky, but this might be Salt and Pepper, or one of the nameless porkies that dwell in these woods. I looked for him again this lonely evening, hoping that the spirit of sympathy might touch his heart and he would come seeking me. But it was expecting too much. My old porky friend did not respond. Whether he had moved away, something had happened to him, or he had forgotten me, I could not know.

When I returned to the island, Salt met me at the landing. His ardor was undiminished, and he talked to me again in those soft, soothing tones.

"Little porky," I said, petting him as he lay quietly over my arm, "the thing you are showing me tonight is our hope in this world. There is something greater than human trials, that overflows them and heals them. You have it, old pal, and you are using it. That you should behave this way is new evidence that there is more to life than the eye can see. My faith rests on what makes a simple little porcupine like you show so much love. This is greater power than bursting bombs. There, there, my buddy, I won't be heavy of spirit any more. These days are not easy, but you point to the guiding star that will lead us through them if we will but be faithful."

Giny had prepared a midnight lunch, and the cabin was lighted with cheer as I returned. She had been thinking too, thoughts provoked by the strange behavior of those two sympathetic porcupines.

The world was not made for loneliness and sadness. Everything works against heaviness of thought. The songs and scenes of nature demand of us good cheer, whatever our lot may be. The world carries on, and whistles as it goes. Giny and I caught the spirit and went about our work. Whatever else was given us to do during these times, being of good cheer was a primary duty.

The porkies looked us over and decided we had taken hold of ourselves once more. They grunted a little farewell, and swam away about their secret business in the great forest beyond.

VII

JUST MAKE YOURSELVES AT HOME

THE red squirrel or chickaree would never draw praise for his disposition. He is the sauciest scamp in the whole forest. He makes everyone—man, bird or beast—feel totally unwelcome in the region which he considers his home. With his own fellows he is extremely belligerent much of the time. You have never had a genuine "bawling out" until you have encroached on the domain of a red squirrel, and he turns loose on you.

Eeny, Meeny, Miney, Mo and Still-Mo had all the characteristics of their kind. They confirmed all the things we had believed about red squirrels, and taught us more. I have never worked with creatures who wanted less "babying." They had brief babyhood, almost no childhood. Giny and I would shiver with concern when we watched the little rascals, not much larger than deer mice except for their tails, racing around the tops of trees at dizzy heights.

From the time the Squints left the cage, they began carving out little individual niches in their island world. There was much squabbling among them. Their differences, like our political issues, were worked out through great oratory, argument and plain bantering. They

65

chased one another about, screamed uncomplimentary things, made long speeches from treetops, and sometimes bit and scratched. But in the end they had accomplished very definite understandings, and I guess if that is the way they must work out their problems we should be content not to criticize. When someone speaks of the noisy red-squirrel squabbles in the forest, I wonder just how a political convention would sound to a squirrel. Maybe it is just as well we don't know what they say to one another, but likewise it is well for our reputation that they do not understand our language when we are in controversy.

After a few days of this wild squabbling by the Squints, Giny and I realized that there was a very tangible result, a definite accomplishment. They had divided our island into five sections, and each squirrel had an area of his own. The cabin vicinity was sort of neutral territory. The feeding station was there, and it was no man's land.

But the living areas belonged definitely to certain individuals. Eeny had taken over the most eastern point of the island, where our campfire parties were held. Her home was the great old scrub oak, near our campfire site. The oak had a homey appearance, and I could understand why Eeny selected it. It looked strong and permanent. Its branches were substantial. When we were choosing an area on the island for our campfires, this one had been selected because of the old oak. It seemed firm, friendly, companionable, and we wanted to be near it. At a crotch in the old tree, Eeny found a little hollow, a ready-made home. She enlarged the opening, did some house cleaning and moved in, obviously very happy in this sylvan mansion.

On the south side of the oak one long limb reached far beyond other trees, so that it was in full sunlight much of the day. Here Eeny loved to spend lazy hours. She was so tiny it was hard to see her twenty-five feet from the ground. But often we would discover her, lying full length on this favorite limb, perfectly relaxed, while the warm sun poured its salubrious rays over her. Near at hand were two towering white pines, and many smaller balsams, cedars and white birches. On the ground beneath were wintergreen plants and bearberries, offering promise of food in the near future. Eeny was so devoted to her oak home that she seldom encroached on the territory of the others.

Mo had settled to the north of our cabin. It was easiest there—he would be so close to the feeding station. He had a hollow white pine to live in, and two old stumps with exposed roots where he could store things. He didn't bother the other squirrels often. It was just too much trouble. Mo spent much of his time yawning. He always looked lazy. When we tapped on his tree, and called him to come down and get a peanut, it would take him so long we disliked to wait. Sometimes he would come part way down the tree, then pause a few feet from my head as if to say, "What's the hurry?" He would hang onto the bark with his hind feet, and stretch hard with his front ones, while he indulged in an immoderate yawn.

Miney had wisely chosen a little hillside just back of our kitchen door. Here was a dense thicket of balsam trees, some birches and maples. I never located his living quarters. They may have been under the house, for he was there a great deal. In fact, that was one of the advantages of his hillside location—he could pass under the house to the feeding station. Miney no doubt got more than his share of everything.

Meeny settled on the northwest corner of the island. From there this troublemaker and born teaser made raids continually on all other squirrel countries. We would hear frantic cries from Miney and look out to see Meeny on a pestering rampage. Next there would be a wild outburst from Mo, and there would go old Meeny racing right through his property. Perhaps three minutes later Eeny would start chattering like an electric riveter, and that prize pest would be down there. It is easy to imagine things when you are watching animals, and no doubt we did in the early days with the squirrels. But certainly it seemed that Meeny made his raids on other territories just to get a rise out of his sister and brothers.

One place he learned to avoid—the land of stubby-tailed Still-Mo. The little high-spirited adventurer had the largest territory of all. He had selected the tree-covered ridge at the southwest corner of the island, including the boathouse. Still-Mo needed much living room. His incessant activity demanded space and variety. Meeny ventured down in the Still-Mo country several times but soon learned better. Still-Mo gave him a chasing he didn't forget. An international agreement was reached between them almost immediately. In plain language it was that Meeny was to stay away from Still-Mo land and mind his own business—or else! Meeny argued against this arrangement for just a few moments. He and Still-Mo crouched facing each other about a foot apart

on a log, each yelling at the top of his voice. Argument proving futile, there was a sudden brief battle, the two of them locked in a scratching, screaming, kicking bundle of red fur. Then the clinch broke, and Meeny made a dash for freedom, the victorious Still-Mo pursuing him up and down trees, through foliage, around stumps, over the boathouse and across the border line into his own country. There Still-Mo paused, mounted high in a hemlock, and in his harsh voice announced to the world that the same thing would happen to any so-and-so chickaree who dared invade his domain. Meeny chattered back brave-sounding statements, but he stayed at a distance. After that there was little trouble between them, except for frontier skirmishes.

But while Still-Mo was apparently the master of the Squints, he was not a bully. He loved his own land, and seldom ventured out of it except to visit the feeding station. In spirit he was much like Duke. He was having a good time being alive. Sometimes other squirrels were with him, obviously just to play. They would race after one another, but in the best of humor, their manners having no resemblance to the heated arguments prevalent when territorial boundaries were being decided.

But Still-Mo the philosopher, the adventurer, the individualist, could be happy alone. We saw him having the grandest times with none but himself and his little world. Red squirrels are always amazing in the way they race through foliage, but Still-Mo was the most expert performer at these gymnastics I have ever seen. I traced his route through the trees one day, and made notes of his startling athletic display.

He was sitting perfectly quiet on a stump, when some plan originating in his mind suddenly animated him. With several little sharp chirps, which might have been the red-squirrel words for "whoopee," he jumped down and raced across the ground toward a large hemlock tree. His little legs moved so fast it was hard to see them, and

his stubby tail was held aloft as if it were a banner. Up
the hemlock he went at a pace fully equal to that on the
ground. At a point about fifty feet high he reached a long
limb which apparently fitted his specifications. Without
a moment's hesitation he ran its length, leaped eight feet
through the air, and caught hold of the tiny twigs at the
end of a birch branch. I gasped.

"Still-Mo, don't do that!" I called, just wasting my
breath.

"Sissy!" he chattered down at me, and away he went.

His route led him through the birch, over another
startling leap to a balsam, then to a young maple and
into a Juneberry tree. Here he faced a problem. The
next tree in the line of flight was a hemlock, and there
was quite a gap. His problem was complicated by the
fact that the limb from which he must make his jump
and the one where he would land were both small and
unsteady. He wasn't sure about the matter. Three times
he ran the length of the take-off branch in the Juneberry
tree, to survey the leap before him. To me it looked impossible. Not so to Still-Mo. He ran to the end of the
Juneberry limb once more and stood poised for an instant. Then he shot through the air with such ease it
seemed the tree had tossed him. Only his front feet
touched the tiny twigs on the waiting hemlock, but that
was enough for him. His little "fingers" clutched and
held and he climbed into the foliage.

Without waiting to rest, he ran on, his route now an
easy one. The trees for some distance had their foliage

interlaced, and he simply ran from one to the other. He ended his wild flight one hundred and fifty feet from where he started, by making a sensational leap to the ground and racing under our house. The little fellow had gone through twenty-three trees of varying size during this run, and he had made four leaps of six feet or over. If ever you want to lose any conceit you may have over athletic ability, just observe the flight of a red squirrel!

One day Giny and I watched Still-Mo in a little stunt that was almost too cute. The play took place at an old stump, and at first we thought all five Squints were there. We saw a squirrel at the top of the stump, then he disappeared and there was one at the bottom almost instantly. Now there was one at the side, then one at the top, then one at the bottom again. As we drew closer we saw what was going on. This was a hollow stump, and Still-Mo had carved it into a playground. He had tunnels all through the decayed wood, and a number of entrances and exits made at the top, at the sides, and among the old roots. Apparently he was trying to be a number of places at one time, and succeeded in giving the impression that he could do it. He would poke his little head out the top, disappear and, quick as a snap of the finger, appear at the bottom. He was having a wonderful time in this little game he had invented for himself. Sometimes he would run away from the stump a few feet, only to make a dash for it, disappear into the roots, and seemingly at the same instant peak out of the top. For days Still-Mo played about this old stump. Occasionally one of the other squirrels came visiting and joined him in the game, but he was content to carry on alone.

So our little two-acre island was converted into a federation of red-squirrel communities. And it is probable that in all the history of our forest never had there been so much chattering and scolding by chickarees in so small an area and so short a time.

VIII

C/O POSTMASTER, SAN FRANCISCO

THERE were occasional letters from Duke as the summer went on. They savored more and more of distance. One told of his return to his unit at training camp. It was good to see his army friends again, he said. His buddy was there and had been nicknamed "Lieutenant Still-Mo," though Duke sometimes called him just "The Loot." The whole outfit had picked it up. The story of Eeny, Meeny, Miney, Mo and Still-Mo had been told and retold in their camp quarters.

"I want to bring Lieutenant Still-Mo to the Sanctuary someday," Duke wrote. "He's a roughneck, but the swellest fellow in the world—the rascal! He would love the forest and be all over it in no time—just like the Squints. You won't get any rest while he is there, but you will like him. Everyone does."

And so it was written in the book of plans that Duke and Still-Mo the Loot were to come to the Sanctuary the moment they had finished their job.

There were other letters from a camp in the western mountains. Special training was being done, but Duke could tell nothing about it. A tone of seriousness was creeping into the lines. Action was getting closer.

One letter seemed like an outburst of Duke's old laughter, and no doubt it had involved a cackle spasm. There had been a week-end leave. Captain Duke and Lieutenant Still-Mo had gone up into the mountains. It was a grand experience. They found a lake, saw a deer, a porcupine, and finally a squirrel.

"You should have seen Lieutenant Still-Mo," Duke's letter laughed. "He said he was as good a squirrel as that one any day, and he started chasing it up a tree. He climbed faster than I ever saw a man go before, but the squirrel left him as if he were standing still. By the time the Loot had reached the first limb, the squirrel had skipped through half a dozen trees. Then the little guy perched on a limb and lectured him—about the way Still-Mo talked to us the day you pinched off his tail. Maybe the squirrel thought that after he had been running after nuts all his life, one had started chasing him. And maybe he was right at that. Lieutenant Still-Mo was thoroughly defeated and looked sort of sheepish when he came sliding down the tree. He said, 'If I'd had a jeep here I could have caught him.' He had to have his uniform cleaned—the rascal!"

There was another letter that said little except to convey a greeting. Duke could not tell us where he was or what was happening. But some way we felt that it was written in a closely confined, heavily guarded place where men were under great strain. We knew well Duke and Lieutenant Still-Mo were on their way—going to do the job they had been trained to do. He gave us a new address—an APO number, "c/o Postmaster, San Francisco, California." He closed it with "God be with you, my friends!" We dispatched an answer which ended "God be with you, Duke—and Lieutenant Still-Mo!"

IX

NOT-SO-GOOD NEIGHBOR POLICY

THE Squints would probably have flown into a rage if anyone had suggested the good-neighbor policy to them. Judging from their actions, all neighbors fit into three classes: those they fear, those they ignore, and those they just plainly dislike. Those they fear are many, though our island offers a refuge from most of them.

The red squirrel must ever be on guard. The hawk and eagle are on the watch for him in the daytime, the owl seeks him at night. Weasel, martin, mink, raccoon, skunk, fox, coyote, wildcat—all predators are on the hunt for him. In the lake waters the fierce northern pike and muskellunge count him a high prize. So old chickaree must be constantly on the alert or he doesn't last long. His quick nervous habits are due to the constant presence of danger. He is always ready to jump, run or hide. It is small wonder that he scolds eternally a world that threatens him so much.

Nonpredatory animals—such as the porcupine, woodchuck and deer—chickaree just ignores. The Squints would race all around Salt and Pepper, paying no more attention to them than if they were tree stumps. Link would eat beside them, and they would neither run from her nor at her.

But as for a chipmunk or blue jay—I dare say the Squints classed them below the lowest form of life. I have often wondered what those red squirrels were saying when they chattered so viciously at a chipmunk that had just taken food they wanted. Doubtless it is as well I don't know, for it would be something not to be repeated, and certainly not to be printed. For the chipmunk and blue jay eat of the food chickaree thinks was created solely for him, and that, in his view, is an unforgivable crime.

We tried, by an adjustment of the food problem, to make the Squints get along well with their neighbors. Perhaps we succeeded to some degree. In the woods at large they sometimes have savage battles with tragic results.

Of course the chipmunk, being much smaller, is generally the victim. But on our island there was not one fatal fight. There was endless wrangling, however. Whenever a chipmunk and a red squirrel saw each other, there was sure to be an argument. Sometimes it was amusing to watch.

The chipmunk has an odd way of extricating himself from a bad situation. He will jump straight up in the air like a jack-in-the-box, a distance of twenty-four inches or more. The action is made with so little effort it looks as if some invisible string had jerked him upward. The chipmunk is the quicker of the two and, I believe, the wiser. He varies his pace, dodges, comes to a sudden stop and reverses with the skill of an open-field runner. His capacity for carrying food in his pouchy cheeks is amazing. Whereas the chickaree can take only one peanut at a time, chippy can take three.

One day I saw the chipmunk we call Beggar Boy provoke Still-Mo until that irritable little rascal almost went insane. Beggar Boy seemed to taunt his rival deliberately. We had tossed out a handful of peanuts on the chipmunk's persistent begging—a habit of his that had led to his name. He had called to Giny and me constantly while we were at breakfast. Because we were more interested in feeding ourselves than in feeding him, he became decidedly impatient. His chirping became louder and louder with insistence. He climbed high in a balsam tree where he could look in at us, and from there kept up his bantering. Finding us unyielding, he ran wildly about, climbed the screen door, raced over the roof. Still he got no results. Then with a marvelous leap he jumped to the window sill outside the screen, opposite our breakfast table.

This was more than Giny could stand. Calling to Beggar Boy lengthy apologies for our neglect, she carried to him a handful of peanuts—such a handful that she dropped one after another as she walked across the cabin floor. Beggar Boy knew what was coming, and ran to the front door to be ready. When Giny threw the precious food to the ground, he darted in and instantly stuffed his mouth so full that his head looked like a toy balloon.

But his calls had brought him something besides this

gift of food. Still-Mo apparently had heard the sound. Perhaps he had a notion there might be something forthcoming in which he wanted to share, or maybe he didn't like a chipmunk talking that way. Whatever stirred him, he was certainly on the war path. He made straight for Beggar Boy, and Beggar Boy headed for the tall timber. There was a brief chase, and Still-Mo lost sight of his little rival. The red squirrel began to eat a peanut. Suddenly Beggar Boy was standing a few feet away looking at him. Still-Mo dropped his peanut and gave chase again. The chipmunk outwitted him. Still-Mo endeavored to eat his tasty snack once more, but there stood that pesky chipmunk looking at him insulting-like. With a scream of rage, he charged the little fellow. Half a dozen times this whole act was repeated, until the red squirrel was so mad he couldn't have digested his peanuts if he had eaten them. He grabbed one and ran away, chattering as he went, while Beggar Boy again stuffed his cheeks to the limit, and began carrying away the rest of the prized food to his underground storehouse.

Other times it was the red squirrel who was chased, and the chipmunk did the chasing. One day I saw Meeny sitting on a log joyfully beginning a peanut feast. He was breaking the shell and dropping the crumbs about his feet. Just as he was about to reach the kernel and reap the reward of his labors, Stubby, our old-time chipmunk, appeared. That peanut looked pretty good to him, and he gave a drooling look in Meeny's direction. It is hard to know what prompted his action. Perhaps it was a moment of supreme courage, maybe the desire for that luscious peanut unbalanced his reason and overcame all caution, or it may be that he instinctively knew Meeny was in a weak mood. Anyway, he dashed at the red squirrel, squeaking a battle cry at the top of his voice. Meeny ran as never a red squirrel ran before. Stubby kept right after him. Meeny did not stop until he was at the top of the highest hemlock tree on the island, and Stubby perched below chortling his conviction that a red squirrel isn't so tough after all.

In the meantime, however, Blooey had swooped down and snatched the coveted peanut!

One sunny morning we noted an ominous silence out of doors. Generally there were calls and cries aplenty.

But no sound is quite so startling as sudden unexpected silence. Not a chipmunk was calling, not a red squirrel chattering, not a bird singing. Giny and I went to investigate. We slipped quietly out of the cabin, hoping not to change the condition until we understood it. We saw Stubby under the corner of the house, still as if he were molded from clay, his eyes fixed on some distant object. Still-Mo hung to the side of a tree, obviously hiding. Link had ducked into her home. Salt and Pepper, with quills raised, were slowly and silently waddling under the house. Blooey let out a single cry and flew fast to the mainland. Beggar Boy came dashing out from among the ferns and disappeared into his underground hideout. Something was present on that island that sent a blanket of fear over all our tiny friends. We began a cautious but thorough search. I thought perhaps it was a weasel, and I had no wish to let one of them be at liberty among our chipmunks and red squirrels. We found Meeny, who, like Still-Mo, was hugging the side of a tree. In a few moments we found Miney, doing likewise. Their position gave me the conviction that the disturbing thing, whatever it was, was in the trees, not on the ground. As the squirrels were all on the north side of their respective trees, Giny and I walked south, now watching the treetops.

Soon we discovered the disturbing visitor. A young golden eagle, glorious in his first year's plumage, perched high in an old white pine tree! Well might our animal friends be cautious when he was around. And what a picture he made, silhouetted against the clear blue sky. For fully twenty minutes he remained there, and complete silence reigned over all the island. Then the big bird spread his great wings and took off. Gracefully he skimmed the treetops and headed determinedly for some distant destination. When he had gone, Blooey came winging back, uttering a cry of defiance which he had been careful to hold while danger was near. Stubby began chirping, and half a dozen chipmunks joined in. Still-Mo and Meeny had a brief fight, Mo yawned and stretched on the sunny side of a tree, Eeny began scolding all eagles north of the equator, and Miney chased two chipmunks away from the feeding station. Things were normal again.

X

A LETTER FROM DUKE

THE summer nights were lengthening and days getting shorter when we next heard from Duke.

"I'm in a ship on an ocean," Duke's good-humored writing ran, "and if anyone can make military information out of that, let them help themselves. At least I guess it's a ship we're on. Sometimes I think they shipped us out in a big barrel by mistake. I hope they remember which is right side up for this tub. It's been on every side since we started. I feel as much at home on the ceiling as on the floor. About ninety-nine percent of the boys are seasick, and that includes Lieutenant Still-Mo. The rascal, am I laughing at him! I turned out to be a pretty good sailor for a fellow who never saw the sea until this jaunt began.

"You'd never guess how we have been spending this evening. I started telling one chap about the Squints and other things at the Sanctuary. I guess I wanted to hear about it myself. As we kept on talking, one man after another pulled up a chair and listened in. Before long we had practically everyone in our outfit who wasn't busy being seasick. Some of the boys had heard me tell the stories before, but they wanted to hear them all again. Then one suggested it would be a swell place to go when we come back. I hope you won't mind taking care of a regiment or two one of these days.

"What impressed me most was the way talk about the woods calmed the fellows down. You may imagine that there is a feeling of suppressed excitement aboard. The men are under a strain, and they try every way to escape from it. But nothing served better to give them relief than simple talk about five baby red squirrels, away up in the north woods.

"I have been thinking much about such things. One of the few virtues of this present experience is that one has time to think. It made me realize how important are the little things in the world. So much of the time we go searching for something fabulous, something that will sweep us off our feet with its size and grandeur. But it is the little things that count.

"To my mind will come recollections of a single little flower, or one lone leaf that I have picked up and noticed closely. I cling to pictures of stretches of trail, or passing moments held in memory for their brief beauty. Little things, of course—but how I reach back for them. When I let myself daydream for a moment and just give way to yearnings, so many of the everyday trivialities come to me. I remember small acts of kindness, friendly greetings and bits of courtesy and politeness that were taken as a matter of course when they happened. But now, when life is so stern and severe, they stand out in memory sparkling like diamonds. Perhaps if we always knew the value of such things we would not neglect them.

"This all seems so clear and true at a time like this. Here I am in the midst of big events. Everything I look on is ponderous, staggering in size and in purpose. Yet I treasure the little things of memory most. Maybe you would write this idea up someday. If you do, please mention how a circle of tough GI's, tossing around on a black sea headed for battle, sat for an evening and listened to the story of Eeny, Meeny, Miney, Mo and Still-Mo.

"So, you see, news from the Sanctuary is important. Send more! Tell me everything that happens there. Give me a complete report on the wild menagerie. There are a lot of fellows here who want to feed their hopes on it.

"But I guess I'll have to cut this short. That last wave we hit leaves me with the feeling that I ought to join the ninety-nine percent. Move over, Lieutenant Still-Mo, you rascal—here I come!"

XI

PEANUT PROBLEM

DUKE'S letter stirred up a new wave of enthusiasm at the Sanctuary. Little had we realized that the simple experiences at our island Sanctuary could be of interest to men facing the severity of war conditions. The Squints must have thought we had suddenly gone crazy. We pursued them constantly with our cameras. We caught their footprints on paper. We measured them, and even cut tiny bits of fur from their bushy tails—all to send to Duke. A regular weekly bulletin was mailed to him, bearing the latest adventures of the five redskins and their tiny pals.

It was the desire for more material for this bulletin that made us prepare a problem for our chipmunks and squirrels one morning. There was no little consternation among them when they came to the feeding station. Not a peanut was in sight anywhere! Eeny came first, sniffed at the scattered cracked corn and the bread crumbs, and then ran away disappointed. Mo looked the situation over, and stretched out on a log in the morning sun. Meeny, Miney and Still-Mo arrived about the same time. They noted the absence of peanuts, blamed it on one another, and for a while there was a free-for-all battle

87

among them. The chipmunks were concerned, but more easily satisfied. Stubby, Beggar Boy, Mrs. Beggar Boy and now Junior looked about for peanuts for a moment, and then settled down to fill their cheeks with corn.

The squirrels grew more insistent, particularly Still-Mo. With his typical aggressiveness he began demanding peanuts. He perched on a low limb outside the kitchen window and scolded Giny who was working at the sink. Still-Mo was becoming a beautiful squirrel. His stubby tail had grown very bushy. His fur was thick, red and very sleek. Giny pampered him a great deal and he seemed to realize it. Hence he turned loose all his persuasive power on her. He whimpered a little as if begging, then he scolded, then he ran all over the screen before her.

"If you'll look around a bit, Still-Mo, you may find a peanut," Giny said. "Now wake up! We want to see how smart you are."

But Still-Mo kept on scolding. He didn't want to prove his smartness—he wanted *peanuts*.

We had prepared a test for our little friends. Near the feeding station we had stretched a rope between two trees, about five feet from the ground. From this rope a peanut had been suspended by a string about two feet long. There it hung, the only peanut on the place, swinging back and forth in the morning breeze. Chipmunks and squirrels had been running beneath it, but so far none had discovered it.

Giny had a difficult time being as severe as necessary

in this IQ test for squirrels. She wanted to give in to their scolding and begging, and toss them peanuts by the handful. But to do so would spoil all plans. No, they had to *search*.

For two hours the lonely peanut hung at the end of that string without being noticed. There was constant haranguing and not a few battles. Then little Beggar Boy ran up one tree, across the rope and down the other tree. He seemed to pay no attention to the peanut. But soon I saw him on the ground, standing on his hind legs and looking up at the prize. Next, Meeny ran up a tree, across the rope, and down the other. Still-Mo tried it, and even lazy old Mo went across the tightrope.

Now Beggar Boy came up from one side, Meeny from the other, and they met halfway across. For just a moment they paused a few inches apart eying each other. Then Meeny made a dash for Beggar Boy, who executed the usual chipmunk safety move of jumping right up in the air—and landed on the ground with a thud five feet below! He was not hurt in the least, and went dashing into the brush, incidentally chasing Stubby before him. But Meeny had made a discovery. There was a real live peanut swinging leisurely back and forth below him. He balanced for a moment on the rope as if to jump to it, but decided that was not the right idea. He ran to one tree and part way down. The peanut was out of reach. He ran beneath it and looked up. It was still out of reach. He ran to the other tree and reached out, but the distance was too great.

Still-Mo appeared on the scene now, and for a moment he and Meeny forgot to fight. Still-Mo jumped for the peanut time and again. He always fell just a little short. While he stood there looking up to calculate the distance, Meeny ran part way up one of the trees and without hesitating jumped out toward the peanut. He lit squarely on Still-Mo. There was a scuffle that started a riot. Still-Mo ran under the house with Meeny hard after him. A moment later they reappeared, but now Still-Mo was chasing Meeny. Stubby saw them and chased both of them. Mo took out after Stubby! For a few minutes everyone on the island was chasing everyone else. And the peanut waved triumphantly in the breeze!

All was quiet for about an hour. Then the little performers started to reappear. Each one went through the same routine when he arrived—Stubby, Still-Mo, Beggar Boy, Meeny, Miney, Mo and now Eeny. One after another they came to the rope, jumped futilely for the peanut, climbed one tree, ran across the rope and down the other tree. So long did they keep it up that I despaired of their solving the problem.

Then Still-Mo justified my faith in his intelligence. He came bounding out of the forest with obvious purpose. I have often wondered what went on in his little mind. It seemed certain that he had thought out his plan. Without the least hesitation or uncertainty he raced up one tree and out on the rope. Fastening his hind feet firmly, he hung head downward beside the string. Reaching out with his front feet, he pulled it up "hand over

hand" until he had the peanut in his grasp. With a look
of triumph he started running down the rope, forgetting
that the peanut was still tied to the string. When he had
reached the length of the string, it brought him to a sud-

den stop, he lost his balance and fell to the ground below.
Hardly had his feet touched the earth before he bounded
up the tree and out on the rope again. He knew how
to do it now. Again he hung head downward and pulled
up the string hand over hand. This time he paused for a
moment, balancing himself marvelously on the rope while
he cut the string with his sharp teeth. When the peanut
was free, he raced away triumphantly, carrying it to his
favorite hollow tree.

And so the problem was solved! Not only had Still-Mo figured it out for himself, but for all the others as well. Chipmunks and squirrels alike caught on to the trick so quickly it seemed sure they had learned it from observing him. We tied as many as twelve peanuts on the rope at one time, and the little busybodies would take them as fast as we put them there. It was a fine display of intelligence. The rope was the scene of some mighty fine circus stunts in the days that followed. Our movie cameras ran hot recording the odd little trick. And here was one more thing to write and tell Duke!

XII

A HOLE IN NOTHING

I SUPPOSE a chipmunk or a red squirrel cannot keep a diary. And if one of them did, I couldn't find it or read it. But I would like to know just what they think of us. Some of it would be all right, and then again some of it might be highly uncomplimentary.

If Stubby, for instance, could jot down his thoughts, there was one hectic day at the Sanctuary that would probably make him write all night long. I imagine the entry might read something like this:

"What's the matter with those half-witted human beings, anyway? Do they try to make life as difficult as possible? I don't want to be mean, but sometimes I run out of patience. The simplest thing in the world would be to toss out peanuts on the ground and just let us cart them away. But no, they have to hide them, tie them up, and make it hard for us to get them. What's the big idea? We were getting along fine at the feeding station, except for those rowdy red squirrels—and then all of a sudden, no peanuts! We go searching around and find one tied to a rope. The only way we can get it is to hang head downward and get dizzy while we pull it up. Then for a while the only way we can get anything to eat is to act like a bunch of trapeze performers. And those human beings just stand off in a corner and giggle and take our pictures! It doesn't take much to amuse some people! Then when we get used to this rope business, they try a new stunt. We come running up to the rope, but there aren't any peanuts. We look around, and there we see a lot of them stacked up in a *hole that doesn't have anything around it*. It's a funny kind of a hole, because it has sides to it made out of *nothing!* You can see through it but you can't walk through it. It doesn't run down in the ground like a hole should, it's just up in the air. It would take human beings to figure out a hole like that, and there was no sense to it. But we got the peanuts out, even if it did take a lot of work. You know the old saying —you can fool some of the chipmunks all the time, and all the chipmunks some of the time—but why those people want to fool us at all I can't make out!"

Yes, Stubby had had quite a time with a *hole surrounded by nothing at all*. So had the other chipmunks and the Squints. For peanuts had been put in a milk bottle, the milk bottle placed on the ground, and the island animal population presented with a problem that was a headache for them all.

Beggar Boy very imprudently ran his nose right into the side of the bottle. It was much more solid than it looked, and he rubbed the bruised proboscis with his little front feet. Then he nudged the glass ever so lightly. The bottle rolled! He pushed some more, nipping at the peanuts. The bottle rolled on a few feet, but the peanuts remained in full sight, yet were mysteriously out of reach.

Beggar Boy chirped a bit and looked the situation over. This was the *oddest* thing he had ever seen. There was a grand pile of peanuts only a few inches from his nose, he could see them plainly, nothing was in the way, and yet he couldn't get to them! He jumped on top of the bottle and dug at the glass with his feet. Never saw anything like it before! It was like a layer of air that had turned hard and he couldn't get through it!

Stubby now came on the scene. His first job was to chase Beggar Boy away so he could have that mound of food. Beggar Boy ran without a fight, as much as to say, "OK, pal, if you can understand that mess, hop to it. It's driving me wild."

Stubby looked the bottle over, rammed it with his nose, scratched it on every side—and then discovered the opening at one end! He crawled part way in until he could reach the peanuts, and filled his mouth in the usual manner. But when he tried to back out, his head with its bulging cheeks was too big to come through the opening! In vain he scratched and struggled. This was plenty of trouble, for a fellow to get into a hole that had nothing around it, and nothing to it, and get stuck there! Besides, there was another threat at hand. Still-Mo was approaching and Stubby could see him plainly through the transparent sides of this new contraption. Reluctantly he discarded his mouthful of peanuts, backed out the neck of the bottle and ran screaming away as if he thought the thing had bitten him. He hadn't found out how to get the peanuts, but he had found out how not to get them.

Still-Mo was greatly puzzled. What he saw so en-grossed his attention that he forgot to chase Stubby. He approached the bottle a step at a time, with that amazing and amusing red-squirrel attitude of caution. He emitted little chirps with each step, his tail jerking as if he made the sound with it. He was fairly close when the bottle rolled off a tiny pebble about two inches in his direction. With a wild outburst of chatter he raced away for dear life, never stopping until he was on the far side of the island high in his favorite tree!

Meeny had arrived now, and looked approvingly at Still-Mo's flight. If this new thing could chase his rival like that, there was virtue in it. With his typical bril-liance, he found the opening to the bottle at once. He sniffed about it and got the irresistible odor of peanuts. He tried to go through the opening, but being larger than a chipmunk, he could only get well started. Suddenly he realized he was stuck! His front feet were of no use to him, being pinned against the glass beside his head! His hind feet kicked up gravel all over the yard! He twisted

and struggled his best, but for a moment the bottle held him. Down a little hill it went, turning the bewildered red squirrel over and over, and finally crashed into a stump! We ran to help him, but he was free long before we reached him, heading toward his corner of the island at a mad pace. He wasn't hurt in the least, so we made no attempt to hold back our laughter. How we wished Duke could have seen *that* one!

The milk bottle was brought back and placed in its first position, to await new advances by the puzzled little creatures. But it was a long time before anyone came near.

Still-Mo was the first to return. I have always considered what he did to be unintentional or accidental—yet we never know just how much calculation is represented in the acts of animals. Sometimes they seem so stupid, sometimes so smart—and I guess that is another way in which they resemble human beings.

Still-Mo circled the bottle several times. The peanuts looked so good! The bottle had been lodged between two stones so it wouldn't roll too easily, for, after all, that rolling was just a little bit unfair. It was bad enough to offer them a *hole with nothing around it,* but a hole surrounded by nothing that rolls away was too much!

Still-Mo stuck his nose in the opening. Obviously he knew he could never get in. Then he began to dig directly under the mouth of the bottle. The dirt flew in a cloud. He kept on digging deeper and deeper, until he was well under the bottle itself. Regularly he would cease his digging and for a few seconds stand back and look around. Maybe it was to survey his work, maybe just the customary precaution of watching for enemies. Then his digging continued. The excavation he was making went farther and farther under the bottle until a remarkable thing happened. I don't know that he intended it, and yet I cannot be sure that he did not. Whichever, the results were to his liking. When he had dug beyond the center of the bottle, it naturally tilted forward, resting in the excavation on the rim of its opening. The peanuts slid forward, and a number of them came out where he could reach them. In the meantime three chipmunks and two other squirrels had come to look on. Still-Mo chased one after another back into the woods before he began taking the peanuts he had earned so well. At that, he got less than the others did.

Still-Mo repeated the performance four times for us. Even if it were an accident and unintended, he was smart enough to do it again. And it is possible that from the first move he knew what was going to result from his digging.

Stubby and Beggar Boy had become a bit more courageous about the bottle by now. It hadn't eaten Still-Mo alive, so maybe it wouldn't hurt them.

Beggar Boy became especially bold—and promptly got himself in trouble. He went completely inside the bottle. What a marvelous place to be! Here he was in a peanut-filled paradise, and no one could get to him. Greedily he filled his mouth with peanuts. We counted them. He had

five full-sized, double peanuts in his mouth at one time!
Seldom have we seen a chipmunk do that.

But now his worries began! He started to go out, but
his head was much too big for the opening. Stubby had
got just his head caught inside, but Beggar Boy had all
of himself imprisoned. He backed up and made a short
run at the entrance. He came to a sudden stop. Then he
dug frantically at the glass with his front feet, but not a
sliver could he get loose. He decided just to *force* his
way through. He placed his bloated head as far down the
bottle neck as he could and began running with his hind
feet. But they were the only part of him that ran; the rest
just stood still! His flying hind feet kicked peanuts hither
and yon, but when he had finished all this effort he was
right where he began! Outside was that beloved forest of
his. He could see his favorite trees, and the patch of ferns
where he hid from red squirrels. But he couldn't get to
them! He was imprisoned in a hole than he hadn't dug,
but it was mighty real just the same, and it had him maybe
for keeps.

After much hesitation he took one peanut from his
mouth and tried to come out. His head was still too large.
He took out another. Still no progress. He discarded
them until only one remained. Then with a little effort,
and some stationary running by his hind feet, he managed
to edge through the little opening to liberty!

The problem was solved from the chipmunk standpoint. Beggar Boy returned, entered the bottle, took one
peanut and came out successfully. Stubby tried it and did

as well. Mrs. Beggar Boy caught on to the idea, and so did Junior.

The excitement was over now. The red squirrels knew how to handle the bottle, and the chipmunks did too— each in his own way. But it was an adventure they would not forget very soon—and neither would we.

XIII

ONE FALSE STEP

ONE cold, misty August day came an experience that has affected my walking for a long time. No, I was not crippled; in fact there was no real physical hurt. But I felt terribly ill, and I wanted to tiptoe for the rest of my life, or step as if I were treading on eggs, or even *crawl*—anything but put my full weight down in a normal stride. Even now I get little chills when I think of it. *I stepped on a chipmunk!* All that great big forest to walk in, millions of acres of land, and I had to bring my big boot down on poor little Beggar Boy.

I guess I wasn't at fault. Of course I didn't want to do it. But it doesn't help much to explain it, for I can never forget that tender frail little fellow under my hundred and ninety pounds of weight.

The chilly weather had something to do with it. There had to be a grate fire that morning. So while Giny was brewing the coffee and getting the breakfast bacon under way, I went for some wood. Beggar Boy wanted to help. He sat on every stick of wood I reached for. When I scolded him and waved him to one side, he stood up on his hind legs looking at me in the cute way that made me want to give him everything he desired. He simply

101

would not take no for an answer. My mistake was that I had brought no peanuts with me. Had I but three to give him, he would have crammed them in his mouth and gone bouncing off.

But that morning he was simply irrepressible. The more I delayed contributing to his need, the worse he became. He climbed to my shoulders, and up on top of my head, pushing off my hat. He sat on the sticks I held in the hollow of one arm. I put him down a dozen times, but he came right back again. I tossed a few pebbles across

the ground, pretending they were peanuts. He scampered after them, and this gave me a few seconds in which to pick up wood. But very quickly he was back again, climbing on me, going through my pockets, scratching my ear, and once nibbling at my nose.

But the pebbles were helping me get my load of sticks. Beggar Boy would run after anything I threw. It really looked stupid of him. He chased stones that were as large as he, seeming to have no idea what they were until he sniffed them. Once I tossed a big block of fireplace wood. He ran after it just the same, discovered it was not a peanut, and ran back to me again.

Finally a last handful of gravel thrown to some distance kept him away until I had all the wood I could carry. Then I stepped backward to go toward the cabin. As I did, a most sickly sensation crept over me. Under my heel I could feel something much softer than the packed earth of our woodpile path. There came a tiny little squeak. Instinctively I bent my knee and fell to the ground to lift my weight from that foot. The wood was tossed wildly. Then I saw my worst fear realized. Beggar Boy was curled up in a little ball, quivering, and giving a pathetic whine. My foot had been squarely on him, and it seemed that the very life had been crushed from him.

I do not know what I said, but Giny came hurrying from the cabin knowing that something was wrong. There were tears in her eyes as she looked at Beggar Boy.

"I presume the humane thing to do is destroy him," I said, though I shrank from the thought. "You need not see it. You go back in the cabin, and I'll take care of him."

But Giny did not approve of my plan. She is so filled with the conviction that health, happiness, life and goodness are the natural constituents of the world that she does not give in to tragedy.

"No!" she said, firmly. "Let's not do that. Beggar Boy deserves a chance. I feel he will pull through. Please—take him into the tent where the other animals won't bother him!"

We picked up the tiny creature and examined him. He was still breathing, though it seemed that he was hurt internally, as he kept curled tightly in a little ball. Occasionally he would shake a little but there was no other movement.

We carried him into Duke's tent house, spread a towel on the floor, and built a warm dark shelter over him made of balsam boughs covered over with a wool cloth. We tried to feed him a bit of water with an eye dropper, but he would not take it. In fact, I felt that Giny's hope was useless, that the little fellow was already gone.

"There seems to be nothing we can do for him," I said sadly, but still Giny would not give him up.

"There *is* something we can do for him!" she said firmly. "There is prayer. He is not beyond the reach of that!"

Yes, there was prayer. He was such a mite to pray over—only a little chipmunk in a vast world, and yet we realized that instant that it was tremendously important to lift him out of his trouble. We must bring him back if for no other reason than to prove that life and goodness are not helpless, that there is something more powerful than the claims of evil. And we must prove that the Creator of this world we live in is not indifferent to the welfare of His creation—that there is a way to reach a power beyond the human when there is need.

We prayed for the recovery of Beggar Boy. We watched over him through the day and the night. But it is probable I would never have written of this incident had it not been for a letter that came the next day. Strange that we are so self-conscious when it comes to speaking of things of faith. But it is usually as Emerson has said, "We are ashamed of that divine idea each of us represents." Something tries to make us timid about our best thoughts, and of late years it has been almost taboo for anyone to admit that he prays. The letter was from Duke. It savored of the South Seas, of jungles and lurking danger. He said little about them, but we could feel them in the background. He had finished his ocean journey and was "Somewhere in the South Pacific." That was all he could tell. He was well; so was Lieutenant Still-Mo.

"Someday I'll tell you what happened on the ocean," he said. "All I can say now is we are grateful to be alive. There was a brief but terrifying experience. Let me tell you every last one of us knelt in prayer. I prayed as I never had before. Lieutenant Still-Mo prayed beside me. One tough old GI came up saying he didn't know how to pray, and wanted to listen to our prayers. We didn't know much about it either, but we tried our best. You get rid of self-consciousness at a time like that. But we came through without the loss of a man, and some call it a miracle that we did. You may be sure there is many a prayer said here in these jungle nights, when everything in the world seems against you, but everything in heaven is in your favor."

So big, strong, carefree Duke was praying! It helped us to know this. He was praying that evil be held powerless, that good triumph. Certainly we could do no less.

Beggar Boy lingered through five days without the slightest change. His little, gasping breath kept on, and at first he squeaked ever so softly, though this sound stopped after two days. In faith we put a saucer of water near him, and kept bread softened in milk where he could get it. It tested us severely as we went hour after hour, day after day, to the tiny creature to find that he lay in exactly the same position.

Giny never wavered in her faith. She prayed constantly. And it seems this is the way such things must be done.

I shall never forget the joy in her voice the sixth day when she went to see Beggar Boy!

"Sam, he is moving, he is crawling toward me. Come quickly!" she cried.

I went quickly, more quickly than I had gone anywhere for a long time. It was true. Our pet was moving slowly, painfully, in pathetic little steps across the floor toward Giny. She was kneeling to receive him, and cupped her hand about him. There were tears in her eyes, but they were happy ones.

"I knew it! I knew it!" she was saying. "Beggar Boy is going to be all right!"

Yet at the moment he seemed far from all right. One little foot was not working at all, his whole body bent in a curve toward the injured side, while one eye was completely closed. But there *was* improvement. He had regained consciousness. There was something to work on now.

Giny held tenaciously to her prayers. Beggar Boy was not saved to be a cripple, she insisted. He must be restored to his full strength and activity.

Each hour there was gain after that. He began eating, ever so little at first, but within a few days he was taking good quantities of food. He even tried, in a pitiful way, to carry some peanut crumbs away and store them in a corner of the tent. His body straightened a bit, and he began to use the one foot that had troubled him. When we entered the tent house he would come scurrying across the floor, and try to jump up in our hands. Still, the one eye stayed shut.

It was on the fifth day after signs of recovery had begun to appear that a great event happened. That was the eleventh day since the accident. Giny went to the tent early in the morning, carrying a dish of warm milk as was her custom. She opened the door, and I heard her cry, "There he goes!"

Beggar Boy had dashed right by her, and out into the woods. He ran awkwardly, but with considerable speed. At first we thought we should catch him and keep him confined in the tent. But he quickly convinced us otherwise. It was time for him to be about his business, and his happiness in his liberty and recovery kept us laughing. The speed with which he went about amazed us, for none of his legs was really working well yet. But they were good enough for him, and he ran back and forth apparently for the sheer joy of being free once more. When in a few moments he ran up to us, we noticed that his bad eye had opened! What happened I do not know. Perhaps he knew of some way of brushing it against trees or ferns to clear the lids. Anyway, he was seeing with both eyes, and running with all four feet—and it was just grand!

Beggar Boy disappeared into the fern-covered hillside where he had dug his home. We did not see him for several days. Then one night when we sat before a campfire we heard a little noise in the leaves. Creeping out of the darkness into the light of the flames came Beggar Boy, searching for food. You may be sure he got plenty. I believe we would have given the little creature a truckload of peanuts if he could have taken care of them. His ailments were disappearing. There was still a bit of a limp in his run, but obviously it was being overcome. The interesting thing was that he came out at night, quite against the habits of chipmunks in general. As we saw him frequently after dark in the following nights, we concluded that he felt instinctively it was safer to be out when his rivals and many of his enemies were asleep.

Before the summer was done, Beggar Boy was completely healed, with only a little scar near the injured eye as a reminder of his accident. He held not the least resentment against me but became the most devoted and friendly of our chipmunks.

In the course of time a letter from us told Duke of this incident, and he replied.

"You may think that experience with Beggar Boy a small matter, but it is important to us here. I have read your letter aloud to the boys, and they want to thank you for it. Our whole lives now are based on proving the power of prayer. Some way, there seems to be no hope unless that is proved. If what prayer represents were untrue, then we would be lost. Prayer proves God, and only the existence of God makes the things we are doing endurable. Beggar Boy's recovery was a victory for us all. Give the little rascal an extra bushel of peanuts for me—and let's all do a lot more praying!"

XIV

"MISSING IN ACTION"

ON A crisp, cool morning the whole world about us had awakened to the fact that we stood in the midst of autumn, and winter was just around the corner. The Squints and the chipmunks had redoubled their efforts at food gathering. Blue jays and crows filled the air with their fall cries. Chickadees gathered in little flocks, carrying on their incessant, soft conversations. Ducks and geese were on the move. Nighthawks migrated constantly from their summer country in the north to their winter homes in the south. Loons were calling the lonely cries which seem to bemoan the passing of summer.

Giny and I had many ways of knowing that the season of snows was at hand. To begin with, our calendar said it was October. We had been watching the Sanctuary hills blaze forth with indescribable color. The shore-line birches, maples, sumacs and aspens had stood in vivid yellows, scarlet, maroon and orange. The old oak at the campfire site flared in flame color. Ferns and wintergreen on the hillsides had formed a mottled carpet of red and chestnut. Acorns and hazelnuts had fallen to the ground. In early mornings our cabin roof was covered with frost, and spider webs, entangling the branches of balsams and pines, looked like delicately spun strands of silver. Nights were definitely cold, days barely warm. Winter stars were peering into the eastern sky in midnight hours—the constellations of Orion, the Pleiades, and the flaming dog star Sirius, stars that sparkle so well in frosty air. And on our desk lay heaps of mail about appointments, train schedules, hotel accommodations and the many other details of our coming lecture season.

Yes, we knew that winter was coming.

"But how do you think those little fellows know?" asked Giny, as we looked on the hectic activity of Eeny, Meeny, Miney, Mo and Still-Mo.

There was no answer, except the vague generality of "instinct." They had never seen a winter before, and yet something deep in them told of a period of food scarcity and cold ahead. They had no calendars, at least none that we could recognize. They paid no attention to geese flying southward, and seemed to take no notice of withering ferns or colored leaves. They had no parents to call them together for family consultation, saying, "Now, kids, some mighty funny things are going to happen. You'd better listen pretty close to what we old folks tell you, or you may get in trouble. Grow yourselves some thick fur as quickly as you can, for soon now you will get colder than you have ever been before. Believe it or not, that lake is going to get so stiff you can walk right across it. Then out of the sky a lot of feathers will come, pure white and mighty cold, and they will cover this whole country in mounds. Better begin rustling up a right smart store of food 'cause these trees seem to go to sleep when cold really hits them and they stop growing things we like to eat. Grab some acorns and put them in your nest. Get yourselves some white-pine and red-pine cones, and a few from the cedars will taste mighty good. Pick up a few mushrooms, and some of those red berries taste sort of good when you get hungry. Now get a lot of food, and we mean a *lot!* Put it in different places, under sheds, in trees, bury some of it—but be sure it is plenty. And we'll show you how to fix up your nest warm and comfy like. . . ."

No—there was no one to say these things to our little Squints. Nevertheless, they knew them. All through September they had been racing around like mad, getting ready for the season of trial and scarcity before them. Their coats had become thick, sleek and wonderfully beautiful. Still-Mo's stubby tail looked like a feather duster, it was so bushy and full. As he skipped lightly about he held it high as if he were proud of it. Mo spent much time in the top branches of the white pine in which he lived, and which he loved so much. He was cutting the cones loose and letting them fall to the ground. We heard the constant thud of them all through the day. Then he would run to the ground to gather them up, often finding Eeny or Meeny there chiseling in on his work. There would be a brief skirmish while the intruders were chased away.

We noted something that was odd about this chasing business. It seemed to be justice that ruled, rather than mere power. Once the Squints had established themselves in various parts of the island, each recognized the local sovereignty of the other. Although Eeny was the weakest and mildest of the five, if even the all-powerful Still-Mo came into her realm she could drive him out. In combat in open territory, no doubt the clever Meeny could have outfought Mo, but when Meeny came under Mo's pine tree and started to partake of the cones he had nipped from the treetop, Mo was master and Meeny ran.

Back of our cabin stands a cluster of white cedar trees. Their lovely palmlike leaves, of rich, vivid green, give a regal touch to the island foliage. To look on these quiet, dignified, beautiful little trees is a nice way to awaken in the morning. Their exuberant appearance in the tinting light of the early sun justifies their name arbor vitae— or "tree of life." When we first come from the cabin in the morning to indulge in the luxury of the north-woods air, it is our habit to gaze on the beauty of this thriving youthful grove.

One morning in autumn we saw that the branches of several of them were shaking and bobbing in a mysterious way. There was no sound, but from the motion we knew that something was going on. We moved quietly to a point from which we could see into the foliage. There were Eeny, Meeny, Miney, Mo and Still-Mo—each in a separate tree, so engrossed in what they were doing that they did not notice us!

Still-Mo was nearest, so we could watch him best. He was racing about in a young cedar, his abbreviated tail waving with enthusiasm. He jumped from branch to branch, then ran up and down the trunk apparently inspecting every inch of the tree. Something seemed to be lacking in this first cedar, so he tried another. It proved more satisfactory. He began scratching frantically at the stringy bark with his little front feet, piling up shreds as fine as cotton. This material he promptly stuffed into his mouth. Then he scratched up some more, and stuffed that in too.

This kept up until Giny and I were afraid his jaws wouldn't stand the strain. He tucked and crammed in more and more of the cedar shreds until they came out the side of his mouth and reached his ears. They heaped up above, covering his nose and eyes. They dragged under his chin until he looked like some bewhiskered little old man. Still he dug, scratched, and forced the cedar bark into his overstuffed mouth. Then he ran down the tree with his funny-looking load of hay and hurried across the ground. Twice he stepped on some of the cedar strings that were dragging and fell head over heels. But he gathered up the bits he had dropped, and continued his journey right up into the hollow of a white cedar where he had made his home. In an instant he was out again, having left the load of shreds behind. Back to the same arbor vitae he went, and repeated his process of woolgathering.

The other Squints were doing the same. Even Mo was busy, though he had found a cedar log on the ground which made it a bit easier for him. Although he worked much at his autumn chores, the frantic industry shown

by the other Squints never gripped him. He would
scratch up a pile and then, like as not, stretch out flat on
his stomach for a few minutes and think things over.

But these bundles of shredded cedar bark were most
useful to our Squints. It was insulation for their homes,
and a warm covering in which they would snuggle when
temperatures of thirty and forty below zero came to the
north country. Still-Mo carried so much of it into his
home in the hollow cedar that I wondered if there were
any room left for him. I climbed up the tree and reached
my hand in, just to feel how conditions were—and he
promptly bit me! I decided to let him run his own home,
which is certainly his right in this democracy.

It was on one of these autumn evenings that Still-Mo gave us a surprise and something of a shock. Giny and I had been canoeing along the far shores of our lake. We had seen several deer and noted that they were wearing their heavy, dark-gray coats, the bucks with fully developed antlers. Beavers were working industriously. And on the cool evening air we heard the bark and howl of coyotes. As we were returning to our island, our path lighted by an autumn sunset, we noted something moving along the surface of the water about a hundred yards from us. The lake was perfectly smooth, and we could only see that there was something breaking the surface, moving toward our island. It seemed to be the dorsal fin of some huge fish. Hoping to get a better look at it, we sculled our canoe in that direction, getting directly in the path of the creature—whatever it was. On it came, without the slightest hesitation. We watched it, greatly puzzled, expecting any moment some great swirl and splash in the water when this super-fish discovered us and took to the depths. But there was no such splash. The creature approached to within thirty feet and still held to its course. It came to twenty feet, ten feet—and finally sailed right beside us, so near we could touch it. There we recognized Still-Mo, swimming nonchalantly, his bushy tail trailing along. The little fellow's speed was remarkable. He was heading determinedly for our island, apparently coming from a smaller island about three hundred yards away. Giny was greatly concerned.

"Still-Mo!" she exclaimed, putting her paddle directly

in his path. "Come out of that cold water! What do you think you are, a polar bear or a fish? Come on, you little rascal, before some musky makes a meal out of you!"

Still-Mo scrambled up on the paddle blade and ran up the handle into our canoe. He looked up at us obviously much surprised to find us there. That moment we realized how little there really was to the tiny fellow. With his fur soaked down tight to his body, he seemed scarcely larger than a chipmunk.

"Let's take him to shore," Giny was saying. "After all, there are muskies and pickerel in here."

I started to guide the canoe to shore, but Still-Mo was not going to be babied like that. He ran along the railing to the bow of the canoe, which was now nearest the island, and without hesitation jumped into the water. Away he went toward shore, and we followed him until he had landed safely. He climbed on a stump, hurriedly combed out his fur with his front feet, chattered a defiance to anyone who didn't like him—and dashed in the direction of his white cedar home! No doubt there were many such journeys by Still-Mo and the other Squints.

Our bulletin to Duke told of these things. He had asked us to write him even those minute details of our north-woods adventures that we might think lacking in interest or importance.

"Perhaps you do not realize how we hunger for news of home," he said. "Even little experiences, and descriptions of what you see so commonly, mean much to us. I feel sometimes as if I crawl right into your letters, and walk among the events and in the places you describe. I used to dream about going to an island covered with palm trees and tropical atmosphere. Now I would trade this whole South Pacific for just one bushel of gravel at the Sanctuary."

So we told Duke about the Squints gathering food and shredding cedar bark. We told him of Still-Mo's swim, and then we had an item of news that probably carried no joy. Eeny and Miney had disappeared!

It happened near mid-October, shortly before we were to leave our Sanctuary for the winter. We had been seeing so few squirrels at the feeding station, we went investigating. Still-Mo was there, so was Meeny, and lazy old Mo hung on the side of the tree just looking at us. But in Eeny's part of the island we had no greeting, except from Beggar Boy and Stubby who kept running all over us. We called Eeny, and tapped with a peanut on the side of the old oak tree in which she had lived—an act that had always brought her to us. But there was no response. A search for Miney was equally fruitless. When several days had passed without the two showing up, we accepted the fact that they were gone. Where and why we could not know for sure. Our fears said to us there might have been hawks visiting the island, or perhaps a weasel, but we could not know. Perhaps they too had been swimming around, and had fallen victim to those musky submarines.

It saddened us more than it should have for these two Squints to disappear. In dealing with forest creatures, one must be ready to face and accept the inevitables of Nature's ways. But we had come to be fond of the little red rascals, and we missed them.

When time had passed for Duke to reply to this news, his letter showed plainly he regretted their disappearance. "At least," he said, "until we know better let's just list them as *missing in action*. This leaves the door open anyway!"

XV

WINTER WAYS AND WOUNDS

THE Squints—however many there were of them remaining—found their first winter in the world to be a dandy. Snows came early and stayed late. The "white feathers coming down from the sky" heaped up in drifts that were small hills. Blizzards howled through the north woods. The thermometer settled well below zero and stayed there most of the time. Roads were blocked, and even the main highways of the region, usually kept open by great plows, were impassable at times.

Deep under this feather bed of snow many of our forest friends slept the winter away. Link, the canny woodchuck, now would be curled in a tight ball in a specially prepared chamber of her underground home, dreaming of a heaven made of carrots and cabbage. Chipmunks were sealed in their caves. Occasionally, though rarely, a place might be found where a little plume of vapor came from a sort of chimney in a great snowdrift. Beneath here would slumber the bear, his alarm clock set for the first days of spring. Deer would be having difficulties with the deep snows. It would be hard for them to move about in search of food. They would "yard up" in small groups, selecting valleys where they remained for the winter. Their tiny hoofs would pound the snow down as they moved about, and if the food of their narrow home gave out, they would be in a sad or even tragic position.

We often imagined what Still-Mo, Meeny and Mo would be doing, though we did not get back to see them. Our winter went to struggling with the difficult wartime transportation problems, bringing to people our message from nature. We found the fine people of the city tired by their efforts—tired but determined. The war job must and would be done. Americans, who had such a distaste for war, must call forth even greater determination than people who had known less freedom. The hour of beauty we might bring them in films of forest, fields, lakes, streams, mountains, dawns, sunsets, was rest and refreshment to them. For the time they could forget the stern and gruesome things they must manufacture to meet the needs of the men at the front. Here they were reminded of the world of nature—the world that God had made—that knew no war but lived on in its unbroken routine. And here was a world to which they could return when the epidemic of fighting was done. With this beauty in mind, they could turn again to their temporary duties better able to carry on.

We felt certain we could picture what was going on at our forest home. The three Squints would not be out every day. During extreme cold they would stay in their protecting nests—Still-Mo in the hollow of his white cedar, Mo in the big hole in the white pine, Meeny in his hemlock. They would curl tightly in the cedar shreds, their heads and noses wrapped up in their tails, tuck their tiny feet in the middle of themselves—and let the winter rage. When things were milder, they would come out. The snows would record their trails as they went from tree to tree. What a brilliant contrast would be their flaming red coats to the white that prevailed over the northland!

But many things went on at the island that we didn't know about until later. Still-Mo, for instance, had taken to living in Duke's tent house. Since he didn't know how to use the door his human friends used, he chewed an opening to his liking—right through the roof! The place made a fine dining room during this severe weather. Into it he carried scores and scores of cones from red and white pine trees. From these he extracted and ate the seeds, dropping the other portions on the floor. A deposit of several bushels of this debris accumulated. Just to play safe, he chewed several other doors through the canvas, one at a new point in the roof, one in the wall at the back of the tent, and one in the side. The fact that snow could get in as well as he could probably did not occur to him, or maybe he didn't care. It may be that he had Meeny and Mo in to lunch occasionally. At least there were enough pine-cone crumbs on that floor to have been the work of half a dozen squirrels.

Salt, or Pepper, or both likely visited the island during the winter. Whoever it was from the porcupine clan peeled much of the bark off Mo's big white pine, and ate the coverings of several smaller trees for good measure.

Only once we heard from Duke. It was a long letter talking mostly of home things, saying little about his own experiences. But some way it bore the echo of events filled with dangers and difficulties. There was the feel of jungle fighting, of soggy swamps that must be traversed in darkness, with desperate enemies lurking on every side. There were the boom of cannon and the rattle of machine guns and the flash of bayonets—not in the things he said, but in what he left unsaid.

"If for no other reason, I am grateful for this experience in that it gives me a better sense of values," Duke said, and I feel sure he was writing in a foxhole. "The boys are finding they do not reach back for the things they thought so important at one time. It is not the glittering and gaudy things they yearn for now—not great positions or possessions. Here where one owns very little, and maybe does not own that for long, he sees that material things are not first in value. It is what the heart holds that we prize.

"Like the man rushing from a burning house grasping the things he really values most, we hold fast that which is highest in our love. And we find it is the love of family and friends, the quiet peace of home and fireside, the simple everyday experiences of normal living that we want. I hope this sanity stays with me when I return. For at this moment I know I am thinking clearly and truly."

Weeks passed. Then from Duke's parents came a message to us that made winter cold deeper, its nights darker. Duke had been wounded in action!

XVI

NO NEWS IS AWFUL

I SUPPOSE the more anxious one is to get news, the harder it is to get. Pining for things seems to be a sure way of not getting them. No doubt the attitude that gets one the best results in this world is to be grateful for what one has. Emerson thought this through clearly when he said, "All I have seen teaches me to trust the Creator for all I have not seen." Patience is not only a virtue, it eases the pressures which anxiety and wanting cause, and is the very key to unlock natural blessings.

But it was hard to be patient about news from Duke. Word was so slow in coming. For days and days we had nothing beyond the first notice that something had gone wrong with him. When additional word did come, it was fragmentary, incomplete and from varied sources. There was a brief note from Duke to his parents, apparently dictated to a Red Cross worker. He was all right, he insisted, and there was "nothing wrong that a cool breeze and a little rest won't cure." A companion wrote that he had seen Duke, insisted that he was doing well, and said that he presumed his folks knew he had been decorated for bravery. But no one at home had heard a thing about it. It had occurred long before the injury, but it was typical of Duke to say nothing of it.

Then there were letters from other buddies and a long-distance call from one who had reached the States. Through these we pieced together a picture that was somewhat guesswork. We learned of a tiny tropical island having enemy installations that must be destroyed; of a volunteer force that set forth to accomplish it—Captain Duke and Lieutenant Still-Mo included. There was a landing in the middle of a night, fierce fighting against an invisible foe, and a tremendous explosion which had to be set off so suddenly that it destroyed not only the installation, but some of the landing party as well. Duke had been tossed far by the concussion. His men found him and carried him back. Lieutenant Still-Mo was missing; it was said that he had run on ahead of all to do the most dangerous part of the work.

The winter snows were melting and the light of spring was in the air when we had our first direct letter from Duke. The handwriting was a little shaky, and the wording heavy for him—but it was from our Duke and it was reassuring. He asked our prayers, not for himself, but for his buddy.

"Lieutenant Still-Mo deliberately did a job I was supposed to do. He did it to protect me. There is no word from him, but I can't give him up.

"I wonder if you could guess what went through my thoughts the night we landed. It was the story of the healing of Beggar Boy! I held to it desperately. It seemed to be the only thing strong enough and real

enough to meet the circumstances. It was this clinging
to prayer that brought me through, I know. Lieutenant
Still-Mo didn't turn wholeheartedly to prayer. He believed in it, but usually wouldn't take the time. The last
words I heard from him were on this subject. When we
were crawling forward, I whispered to him that he had
better say a few words of prayer. He laughed and said,
'You say a couple for me—I'm gonna be busy.' That is
what he asked, and that is what we must do."

As to himself, Duke insisted he was all right. Just
suffering from shock and nervous reactions. But there was
not a characteristic giggle in his whole letter.

Later another letter came which had a bit brighter tone.
He expected to have a leave to finish his job of getting
well. He would arrive along with the springtime, and
could he spend part of his time at the Sanctuary? It was
the thing he wanted most, next to seeing his family.

Could he? If we could have shoveled up our whole
Sanctuary and given it to Duke, we would have done so.
We couldn't reach him with our reply, as he was on his
way, but we left word at his home that the place was his—
to come when he could and stay as long as he wished.

I believe there is no other joy available to those who
remain behind quite equal to serving in some way the
boys who are carrying the burden. Our hearts fairly sang
as Giny and I cut our work in the cities short to return to
the Sanctuary and make ready for Duke. Everything
must be better than it had ever been before! The beauty
must be polished up, the peace and solitude deepened, and

we hoped in our hearts that Nature would be in her funniest mood.

For it seemed to us that even the springtime songs of the meadow lark, olive-backed thrush and oriole would sound less beautiful than one of Duke's cackle spasms.

XVII

SPRING CLEANING

IT WAS A somewhat disorderly forest we gazed on when we returned to the north country. The woodland floor looked as if nature had swept all her dirt under the carpet of winter—and now this covering had been whisked away. Crumpled fern fronds and old leaves lay matted to the earth. Shapeless clusters of last year's grass were heaped along the shore line, as though yesterday had tossed her toggery carelessly to the winds. Along the shores rolled driftwood at the finger tips of the waves, like toys discarded by the waters. Trees had their hair up in rag curlers, the leafless branches standing straight and stiff in the springtime sky. Over the countryside hung a blue haze drifting down from some faraway forest fire, a veil through which the sun peeked weakly. And it seemed that nature had no curtains at her windows, for we could see far back through shore-line groves to the hillsides that were obscured when summer foliage draped the landscape.

As our canoe approached the island everything combined to make us feel we had slipped up on nature when she wasn't expecting us. There were distant calls from ravens, crows and blue jays, but not a creature met us as we landed. In earlier years Salt and Pepper, or Inky, or one of the other animals had been at the shore to greet us. But now there was not even a chipmunk.

"What is the matter here?" exclaimed Giny, as we set our luggage ashore. "Surely someone is around. Stubby! Beggar Boy! Still-Mo! Where are you?" she called.

But her only answer was an echo bounding around the near shores saying, "Are you? Are you? Are you?"

Even our cuddly little cabin seemed to yawn and stretch as we entered, its doors creaking a mild objection to being disturbed so early in the year.

But we have learned there are two things to do to take the chill of disuse from a house. One is to light a fire, the other to have a bite to eat. It doesn't need to be a big fire, or much of a meal. The important thing is that you have added something of your own to your surroundings to make you a part of it.

Giny and I have a get-acquainted routine as we enter our home after an absence. We do not unpack at once. First, there must be a grate fire to send its warmth about the room, while the tongues of flames gossip about everything that has happened in past months. Then there must be a hot beverage—coffee, tea or a cup of soup. We rescue two chairs out of disorder, and there in the midst of a thousand things to do we sit before the fire and sip and talk. Every warm swallow carries us farther into our home, and cuts away the feeling of strangeness. It is toward the bottom of the second cup, near the ashes of the third armload of wood, that we get that "completely moved in" feeling.

And it was near the bottom of our second cup of tea this morning that things began to happen normally about the cabin. Several blue jays lighted in a tree near the feeding station, and Giny had to hustle some bread crumbs to them. This was normal. Seldom in the past had we finished a meal without some creature demanding service. We had resumed our sipping when a little sound drew our attention to the window. There we saw a funny little face peering in at us. There were tiny beadlike eyes, small cupped ears, and a face so smeared with mud we couldn't tell its color or shape. But back of it we saw sticking up a thick bushy red tail with a cluster of black hairs at its tip!

"Still-Mo! Still-Mo!" we cried in unison.

Giny swallowed her tea so quickly it burned all the way down, and I spilled mine in my lap as we rushed to the door to see our friend. He was so startled at this excitement he disappeared under the house. In a moment he was back, however, chirping little questions as he advanced cautiously toward us. He wasn't quite sure at first. Lots had happened since he had last seen us. The problems of the winter had made him wary and perhaps had caused him to forget some things about our companionship.

Now both Giny and I were in the yard kneeling, coaxing him to come to us, and offering him peanuts which we had made sure to bring along. He was inching toward us, terribly excited and anxious, but ready to make a hasty retreat if things didn't look right. He moved up until his mud-spattered nose touched the peanut Giny was holding. For a moment all three of us became perfectly still. Still-Mo took the peanut gently. He sat up and turned it over and over in his front feet, thoroughly examining it. Then with sudden enthusiasm he took it in his mouth and went skipping across the ground, chattering his delight.

Giny and I placed more peanuts on the ground, and now went happily about our work of getting life started at the cabin. Our first pet had returned, so the season had begun. Still-Mo did not give us a chance to forget that he was there, either. When the supply of peanuts ran low, he told us about it in his own way. He ran up and down the screen door, across the roof, jumped up on the window sill, and when we had left the door open for a moment he came inside and ran all over everything.

Within an hour both Stubby and Beggar Boy had put in an appearance. It was another moment of excitement when we saw them. They had little trouble in identifying us. For just a moment Stubby stood studying us in silence. Then, sure of himself, he ran straight to me and jumped on my outstretched hand. Here he sat, loading his mouth with the nuts I held for him, with as much confidence as he had when we last saw him months before. When Beggar Boy saw us, he did not even hesitate. Coming from behind me, he jumped as high as he could, catching a foothold in my clothes, then climbed to my shoulder and to the top of my head. He still favored one leg a bit, though he ran well. There was the scar on his face, too, but otherwise he was a strong, healthy and apparently happy chipmunk.

As hours went by, more chipmunks and more birds reported in. Mrs. Beggar Boy and Junior were there and several new ones. But we came to realize that Still-Mo was the only one of our Squints remaining. Meeny and Mo, who had been there in the autumn when we left, were "missing in action." Where and when they had gone we could only guess—and our guesses were not very pleasant ones.

We missed the little red rascals. We had learned to know our Squints well, and when one learns really to know anyone in this world, one is bound to love him. The more I see of life, the surer I become that it is more important to love than to be loved. If there were no other benefit, that fact justifies the love of nature and her creatures. It is just plain *good* for us to love. Whatever it does to that which is loved, it frees within ourselves greater health and happiness, enhancing our talents and abilities. I could not guess how much affection we rated with the Squints. Perhaps to them we were just a fine supply of peanuts. Maybe the idea of actually caring for us never entered their little self-centered red-squirrel minds. But that did not matter. I felt like saying to them, "Go on, think as you please about me—that is your own affair. Just remember, though, it is none of your business if I love you." From our viewpoint they were something to love, and so they were an opportunity.

Life at the Sanctuary now got under way. Every hour

things became more beautiful. The woods underwent a thorough house cleaning and straightening up. Spring washed the countryside down with driving rains, then polished it up with sunshine. With its winds it dusted off the forest and brought forth leaf buds on barren twigs. New grasses and ferns came out in great numbers to change the forest floor from brown to green. Waves of warblers flew through the enlivened trees, breaking silence with the sweetness of their song. Starflowers, spring beauties, lilies-of-the-valley and the sweet-scented arbutus came forth to perfume the air. The atmosphere was cleansed of its smoke haze, the sun shone brilliantly from flawless blue skies. In a few days nature's house had been set in order and everything was busy growing.

Giny and I had been about as busy as spring itself. The day neared when Duke was to arrive. Several telegrams told of his coming, and how anxious he was to get there.

We had lots of help in our work as usual. I had to patch up the holes in Duke's tent which Still-Mo had made. But for a while he kept pace with me. As fast as I patched one, he chewed another! I finally discouraged him by placing squares of screen wire on all of his approaches to the tent. After that he gave it up for the time being. Boats had to be painted, and Stubby helped with that by tipping over a can of paint. Giny hung out some washing between two trees back of the cabin, and Still-Mo promptly chewed the clothesline in two and dropped the clothes on the ground. Things were getting back to normal all right!

"Well, it's something to tell Duke, anyway," Giny had said about her clothesline disaster.

We found that was the way we were thinking about all events—in terms of sharing them with Duke.

So it was that the last night before his arrival we sat together at the fireplace and made a list of all we should tell him! We hadn't seen Salt and Pepper, the pesky porcupines, but from down the shores of a lake had come a story that indicated they were at large. Here a man had returned to his woods cabin for just a few days' vacation. The first night he had heard a noise on his back porch. Looking out, he saw two porcupines sitting there looking up at him. Puzzled, he opened the door. The porcupines promptly came in, filed past him without so much as a greeting, went on into his living room and sat down before the fireplace! He didn't know how to talk to them, he didn't know how to *shoo* them, and certainly he didn't know how to pick them up nor did he want to try. Finally, with the aid of a broom, to the tune of much indignant grumbling by the porcupines, he managed to push them out.

Duke would get a laugh out of that, we reasoned. Also, Blooey was back putting on comedy stunts. He was catching peanuts as we tossed them in the air, and was constantly making life miserable for Still-Mo. Link had showed up looking like some hobo in the loose folds of skin that hung about her since hibernation. We wished we might have a way to call all the woods creatures together and tell them they must be their funniest—for Duke must laugh.

But we had something to learn about Duke—something quite painful.

XVIII

A STRING THAT STRETCHES

DUKE arrived on the kind of a morning we wanted for the occasion—the kind we call a "Diamond Day." The sun was strong and warm as it peered over the pines along the eastern shore. A light breeze blew from the north breaking the surface of the lake into myriad wavelets, each crowned with a jewel, the gift of a sunbeam. The living world swelled with life. Buds were now expanding into leaves, unfolding into the forest pattern an infinite variety of colors and shades. Birches and alders were festooned with catkins like silken cords. Maple leaves peaked out on the world in delicate rose hues, even rivaling their brilliant autumn shades. Young aspen leaves, dressed in lush green, quivered in the morning breeze. Oak leaflets proudly displayed their russet brown. The whole north country hummed with the industry of springtime. Overhead hung the last quarter of an old moon, defying the sunlight, as if it were reluctant to lose sight of this lavish display of loveliness. Birds were singing in such chorus it was difficult to separate their songs sufficiently to identify them.

Duke was wandering about the cabin grounds while Giny put the finishing touches on the first breakfast. We caught glimpses of him through the various windows. It

was obvious that he wanted to shake hands with all the
growing and living things that stood before him. I saw
him walk up and pat the white pine where Mo had lived.
He stooped to touch a baby fern that was unfurling at his
feet. Every step he took was dogged by Still-Mo and a
half-dozen chipmunks, and he knelt frequently to feed
them and let them run all over him. I saw him literally
take a young cedar tree in his arms, bury his head in its
foliage and crumple a few leaves between his fingers to
release the pungent odor. At the lake shore he stood for
some minutes, arms folded, feet spread and firmly fixed
in position, looking as if it would take a tank to move him
an inch. His eyes feasted on the beauty of distant shores
and plucked the jewels from the tiny waves.

Duke really looked fine. He had lost a little weight,
and his hands shook a bit occasionally, but his strength
had proved superior to his war experience and he was on
the mend.

"I'm all right, you good people," he had said on his
arrival. "Don't think you have to baby me. Let's just
forget that anything has happened, and carry on as we
always have. All I want to do is scoop up armloads of
this north-woods quiet and eat it down! Now don't worry
about me. I'm OK."

Yes, he was OK—in every way but one. Within our
hearts Giny and I felt sad over the exception. Somewhere
in the trying and tragic months now past, Duke had lost
his natural joy. The lighthearted, carefree humor through
which he had spread so much happiness was gone. His

appreciation of what is good and beautiful in the world
was, if possible, deeper than ever. But the ready laugh
and ready wit were somewhere behind a curtain of heaviness. We felt that only part of our soldier had come to
visit us. Even in those first hours, when the excitement of
his return was at its height, his eyes would become distant,
and his thoughts stray far from the things about him.

Giny could hardly hold back the tears as we faced the
realization that the war had blasted away Duke's youth.

"But it isn't lost," whispered Giny. "It is only asleep, I
am sure. We can awaken it while he is here—we simply
must."

But sometimes I wonder about these human plans—
they are so easy to make, and often so impossible to exe-
cute. Maybe, if we are honest, we must admit that we
human beings are not so smart after all. There are "ways
higher than our ways," and perhaps instead of forcing
things too much out of our own wills, we should clear the
way for right unfoldment by simple faith in the operation
of a Perfect Power. Wise men, through the ages, have
spoken of this fact. And the man who did the most for
the world said, "I can of mine own self do nothing."
Before the truly important things we are helpless, except
through our prayers and faith. We cannot make the seed
grow, we cannot make life live. We are but witnesses to
the great important facts of the universe in which and
with which we live. And there is given us the key to
harmonizing ourselves with creation's ways—that is hum-
ble devotion to the Creator.

I am afraid I forgot these points in the first hours Duke
was with us. I was so anxious to see his old buoyancy that
I tried to force it out of him. The story of the way Still-
Mo had come back to us was told him, with embellishments. A year before, Duke would have entered the story
with eyes sparkling, he would have added many comments
of his own, pictured dirty snoot and bushy tail in cartoon
style, and led everyone in a grand laugh. But now he only
smiled. Then came that distant look, and he whispered
so softly I knew it was not intended for my ears, "Still-
Mo!" Blooey did his tricks, and I pointed out how he
pestered our red squirrel. Duke chuckled a little, but I
felt he did it only because he thought it pleased me. The
story of Salt and Pepper appearing at a neighbor's cabin
drew only a smile and the comment, "Good old Salt and
Pepper—so they are still alive!"

There was one little stunt I had been saving for Duke's
arrival. Still-Mo was to be the victim of a teasing trick
that may have been a little mean, yet I believe the squirrel
never thought of it that way. It was just another problem
for him, and he was accustomed to problems. I tied a
peanut on a long rubber band and fastened the other end
of the rubber to a root. Still-Mo came running up to the
peanut, cocky as usual. He had to chase the chipmunks
away in order to have all the trouble to himself. Then he
grabbed the peanut in his mouth and started away on the
dead run. The rubber band stretched and Still-Mo ran
until the band reached its limit and brought the surprised

squirrel tumbling head over heels to the place from which he had started!

Still-Mo sat up and blinked his eyes. He wasn't sure just what had happened. There lay the peanut, harmless as could be. Surely that thing couldn't toss him for a loop like that. He straightened out his ruffled hair, and thinking this must have been all a mistake, he snatched the peanut again and made another run. Again he came head over heels back to his starting point. With a burst of temper he tried it once more, with the same result.

This was becoming monotonous, as well as ridiculous. He had buried those peanuts by the score and never had one acted that way before. Maybe this was some special kind; maybe it wasn't dead yet.

He began crawling toward it in that comical cautious way of his, just as he had approached the milk bottle. Giving those little fretful chirps which register curiosity, concern, anxiety and temper all at once, he crept up to the innocent peanut an inch at a time. Cautiously he picked up the peanut and examined it thoroughly. The rubber band resembled the strings he had known in other problems with peanuts. On those occasions when the string was loosened the peanut was free. Hence he pulled with his teeth at the part of the rubber that was wrapped about the peanut. It stretched, and so he figured that was loose enough. Slowly now he began making away with the nut. The band tightened, and he felt the pull. He paused, obviously puzzled, then went a few steps farther.

The pull of the rubber increased. Maybe he hadn't
handled that string just right, so he sat up to take the nut
in his front paws once more and look it over. But the
rubber promptly snatched it from his grasp and tossed it
away from him.

Now Still-Mo was downright mad! Sitting up and
folding his front feet on his breast, he turned loose an
uncomplimentary chatter directed at everything he could
see and everything he couldn't. After the peanut he went
again, this time backing away with it in his mouth. The
rubber band snatched it from him once more. Still-Mo

literally pounced upon it then. If the thing wanted a fight, it could have one.

For a moment it seemed that he intended to bury it right where he picked it up. Holding it firmly in his mouth, and chattering his ill-humor, he began digging what was apparently meant to be a grave for that stubborn nut.

But suddenly he spied Blooey overhead, watching every move! If he buried the prize there, the wicked old bird would have it in no time. Forgetting his experience of a few moments ago, the irate red squirrel started up a tree with the pestiferous peanut in his mouth. The rubber band promptly brought him back to earth in no gentle manner.

Now what to do? For a moment Still-Mo was either discouraged or frightened. He dashed away at such speed it seemed he may have thought the peanut was chasing him. But now came Blooey's chance. There is nothing finer in a blue jay's life than to snatch food left by a red squirrel. Down swooped the old rascal, and with marvelous quickness and skill he scooped up the troublesome nut and began his flight. The rubber band was no respecter of persons. It promptly snatched the nut from Blooey's beak. Blooey's persistence was not equal to Still-Mo's. Once was enough. A peanut with a disposition like that probably wouldn't digest very well anyway, so he decided to have nothing more to do with it. But he wouldn't leave without expressing his opinion. With obvious anger, the bird flew down and lighted on the ground near the nut. He hopped to within about a foot of it, and stood there turning his head from side to side as he looked it over. Then he stretched his neck out until he was within a few inches of the aggravating thing and gave that blue-jay scolding cry which tells so much so briefly. Away he flew then, disappearing through the trees toward the mainland.

By this time Still-Mo had returned. As usual, he had thought out the situation and come to a solution. He took the peanut up in his forefeet and sat right there while he cracked the shell and ate the kernels. Then he gave the empty shell back to the rubber band and ran away on other business.

Duke had watched this whole comedy with apparent interest, but little laughter.

The first day had come to a close. Giny, Duke and I sat before an active grate fire, singing some old-time songs to the accompaniment of a guitar. Then came one of those periods of silence which are as much a part of true companionship as conversation. Sometimes I think of this as one of the tests of true friendshp. With acquaintances we must always be saying something, and silence seems to be evidence of indifference or disinterest. But with a friend who is proved real and true, we are not afraid of the wordless moments. Sometimes it is then that the heart speaks plainest.

Duke had leaned forward resting his head on one hand.

Giny was looking meditatively into the fire. I strummed chord sequences on the guitar. It was many minutes before a word was spoken and then our captain broke the silence.

"Um—um, this is grand!" he said, his words preceded by a sigh. "This is the medicine I need. How I dreamed of such things in all that—that bewildering confusion!"

Giny and I looked toward Duke and smiled our thoughts. This seemed a better way to tell him how grateful we were that within our simple possessions there was something of use and benefit to him.

In our rather futile plans for his stay, there was another item that went awry. We had determined we would not talk of war. Others had advised us that the boys did not want to speak of their depressing experiences. But Duke held no such aversion. He began talking easily, as if it gave him release to share his adventures. For nearly an hour he talked, interrupted occasionally by a question from Giny or me. It was simply a recital of facts. There were no heroics. He told anew of the adventure at sea, when their boat was tossed around by the near misses of bombs.

"We didn't come through on a wing and a prayer," he said in calm conviction. "It was prayer and nothing else."

He spoke warmly of the character and fighting qualities of his men, the way they volunteered for dangerous missions, and the way they carried them out.

And there was Lieutenant Still-Mo! Duke's eyes moistened a little at mention of his name. The tougher military life became, the better the Loot looked.

"He was—" Duke paused, bit his lip, and corrected himself—"he is such a human guy," he said with emphasis, "always facing things honestly, even-dispositioned, and always doing more than his share."

Then in sporadic sentences came the review of the story of the tragic mission. It was much as we had heard it. It was a tough assignment, and they all knew they would need the help of heaven to pull them through. In Duke's words we could feel the mystery, darkness and potential trouble on that far-off tropical shore. There were friendly native troops who co-operated.

In rich praise Duke spoke of Lieutenant Still-Mo's heroism, his quick decision and self-sacrifice.

"Do you know for sure what happened to him?" I asked.

"No," declared Duke, "no one was sure of anything right then. We knew we were discovered, and we had to act quickly. I was knocked out and the men carried me back. They looked for him, but couldn't find a trace. Nothing has been heard since."

There was quiet again for a moment, and then Duke spoke words strengthened by one of his broad smiles. "It helps to talk of those things. I can't ignore them and run away from them. Thanks for listening."

"Bless your heart, Duke," said Giny, "we love to listen

if you want to talk. We want everything to be the way you want it."

"Yes," said Duke, "I realize you do. And I have been wanting to ask you—please don't try too hard to entertain me. I know I have lost something. But if you don't mind, I would just like to work it out. I feel such a yearning to get into these woods, and just think and *think!* That is the way I want it, and I would feel hurt if I burdened you at all."

That moment our plans were tossed into the fireplace and went up in smoke.

"Duke, old top," said I, "the whole place is yours. Just use it the way you want to. The boats, canoes, trails, trees, animals, and Giny and I are yours to command. You outrank us, boy. You have only one restriction here—you simply have to do as you please."

"My, that's swell!" said Duke, rubbing his hands together. "You see, I've been planning this ever since I knew I was coming back. I dreamed about it on the way. You are so understanding always, I know you will understand this too. I want to be *alone* in the woods. You have work to do, and I don't want to draw you away from it. Anyway, I want to be alone until the roar gets out of my head. I have been seeing people by the thousands and thousands, always excited, always under pressure, no chance to think. It has made me feel separated from things that are real. Yes, I have lost something, or maybe just misplaced it. I know where to look to find it—right

in myself. But I feel sure the way to search is to be alone
—alone where it is quiet."

There was a glow of joy within us as we listened to
him talk. The victory was half won in that he recognized
what must be done. The primary power of problems is
when they rest in darkness and hide from our attention
or recognition. When they are faced without fear, the
strength to cope with them springs forth from our spirit.

Again there was silence for a few minutes. The firelight set shadows to dancing about the cabin walls. The
mantel clock seemed to tick with increasing volume. I
wonder if a clock ticks always in the same way. It seems
to me ours does not. And its quarter-hour chimes likewise seem to vary in musical quality. That clock seems
to love moments when the mood is rich with thought,
beauty and understanding. During lighter times it ticks
and bongs away unnoticed. But let something be said that
savors of spiritual truth, so that we are all carried into
depths of thought, and its *ticks* and *tocks* stand out as if
it were trying to say, "You've got something there." Then
its chimes speak a definite "Amen and Amen."

That was the way the old clock ticked as we sat there
meditating on Duke's words.

"Duke!" I had broken the silence.

"Yes."

"Have you ever looked up the word *alone*—do you
know its derivative?"

Duke shook his head.

"Well, if you did you would understand why you feel

you want to be alone. It is made up of two little words glued together: *all* and *one*. Our natural desire to be alone is that we instinctively want to be *all one,* that is, complete in ourselves, no part of our true selfhood lacking. Among people, we have so many little nips taken out of us, and we are always reacting some way or other to the opinions people hold of us. This leads us to feel incomplete, sometimes to be something other than what we are—at least, not the complete *one* we have been created. Your thought is calling for you to be *all one,* your complete selfhood, which you can see clearest when you are alone and quiet. You are going back in the woods not to sweep up little pieces of yourself and paste them together, but to get rid of things in your mind, little illusions that say you have lost some part of your individuality. You need to be, and you are *alone—all one.*"

"My!" said Duke, looking up. For the first time there was just a faint glint of the old-time twinkle in his eyes.

XIX

TRAILS AND TALES

To THE west of our island, beyond a narrow stretch of water, we look upon a fine forest. Across its groves of pine and hardwoods come the glory of northland sunsets. There we find an abundance of the treasures the north woods have to offer. There are mossy glens, tree-covered hills, life-filled swamps and carpets of ferns and wild flowers. Deer, bear, wildcat, lynx, coyote, wolf, beaver, otter—animals native to this country—are still there in sufficient numbers to be seen occasionally.

Into this region we have threaded many trails for our convenience. They lead over chosen routes to selected spots. One circles through hemlock colonnades, skirts a swamp that in spring is filled with wild iris blossoms, and climbs to a hilltop from which our lake can be seen. Another threads its way over birch-crested ridges and reaches Vanishing Lake, where dainty orchids bloom in July. Yet another reaches into far-flung bogs through which is a great deer runway. Lesser trails take off from main ones leading to sequestered points that have caught our fancy for some reason or another.

It was into this network of trails that Duke went daily. Sometimes he was gone from dawn to dark, sometimes for only a few hours. Two appointments were definite— early morning for breakfast, early evening for dinner. In a little packsack he carried with him bird glasses, a lunch prepared by Giny, a notebook, a compass and certain chosen books rich in thought. And there was one more item very vital for that season of the year—a bottle of savory liquid which, when rubbed on face and hands, caused the mosquitoes to stay away. For at that season these little dive-bombing pests are numerous and savage.

With this equipment Duke was ready to make good use of his hours in the forest. Sometimes he traveled far, coming home with the peculiar tiredness that is laden with blessings and is a kind of rest in itself. Sometimes he sought a comfortable spot—a moss-covered rock, a cushioned log—to sit, think, read and let the world flow by him. His decisions were by impulse and whim, not by strict plan. One morning he had thought to go to Vanishing Lake and explore its interesting shores, but a blue heron flew by and carried his thought in another direction —so he went on the new course. If he had thought to go where he could watch the red-fox den on a distant hillside, and decided he would rather take a swim instead— he took the swim. There were no orders, no military rules and regulations. We had said he was to do as he pleased, and certainly he did a masterly job of it. Seventeen days he was to have, and he declared he wanted to make an eternity of it.

But I learned quickly that I was to have a definite place in Duke's routine. When I heard him land at the boathouse with his canoe or boat, returning from some forest experience, I pushed my work back and waited. I knew what was coming. Almost anything might be placed before me for identification or explanation. Sometimes he brought in little objects—a cocoon, a twig, a leaf, a feather, a flower, a stone. Other times he had just made notes or drawings of something that had engaged his attention.

"I saw the funniest-looking little critter today," Duke said on his return from one journey. "No sense in wasting fur on anything like him. He wasn't so large as a mouse, sort of brown on the back and gray beneath, seemed to have no eyes or ears, and a nose that looked as if it had been sharpened on a grindstone. There wasn't enough of him to be a mole, or he'd have been one."

"Where did you see him?"

"On the sunny side of a hill back in the hardwood country. I almost stepped on him, and boy, did he dive into a hole under an old stump!"

Then Duke would sit and take notes on the explanation. This time it was a shrew he had found, one of the tiny little fellows that are somewhat robbed of their identity by most nature lovers. Many who see them about their wide range —all over the north and central part of the continent— call them moles, or little mice. But they constitute a family all their own. It is easy to distinguish them. First there is their size. They are so small—the common ones about four inches long, and an inch and a half of that is tail! Their little front feet are like those of mice, though in no way similar to the paddlelike forepaws of a mole. Their sharp noses, and eyes, and ears that are well hidden, give them an appearance not like any other creature. They do not burrow, but sometimes enter subterranean runways of moles, or the tunnels of other animals. Their food consists of any kind of meat they can get. Due to their diminutive size they prey on only bugs, grubs, worms and the like. They are pugnacious little fellows, and fights they have with anything near their size usually result in victories for them. They have learned the trick of making themselves undesirable as a meal for most predators! Certain species of them have glands, usually on the sides of the body, which emit a noxious odor when the animal is frightened or enraged. Due to this, most creatures of the forest are satisfied to let them alone.

"All right," said Duke, finishing his notes. "Now I

know what a shrew is. I used to think a shrew was just a wife that gets beaten up in one of Shakespeare's plays. Now—what is this?"

He placed before me a little green plant with wide, thick, glossy leaves.

"Break one of the leaves and smell it or taste it, and I think you will know, Duke," I said.

He did, and contemplated the odor thoughtfully. "Wintergreen?" he asked.

I nodded.

"And another thing," continued Duke. He was filled with questions that day. "I saw a nest high in a tree and when I examined it I could see what I thought was a snake hanging over the side. I thought maybe there was trouble up there, so I climbed to it. There I found a newly built nest, with a piece of snakeskin woven in and hanging down. Now what about that?"

"The nest of the crested flycatcher, Duke. It's a common trick of this peculiar little bird. We can only guess why he does it, but it seems certain he selects the snakeskin for some reason other than to get nest-making material. It is entirely possible he does it to keep certain enemies away—blue jays, crows, squirrels or chipmunks."

Now Giny was calling that dinner was ready, and as usual we were ready for dinner. But Duke had another observation of the day which must be talked out.

"I landed with the canoe on Sunset Point," he said, indicating a point of land which reached well toward our island. "There on a low limb of an oak was a red squirrel that was quite small. When I saw it, I found myself calling it Mo. I don't know why, but it looked like Mo. Certainly it acted like the lazy old rascal. It just hovered close to that limb and looked down at me, blinking the way Mo used to do. Do you suppose it could be the little guy?"

I shook my head. "Not a chance in a thousand, I would think, Duke. And yet I wouldn't want to say absolutely no. We really know so little about animals. It's my guess we have seen all we shall ever see of those Squints who have disappeared."

"Well, how could I know for sure?" Duke persisted, while Giny kept calling that dinner was very ready.

I thought a minute. "Peanuts would prove it," I said. "No wild squirrel in this region knows what peanuts are. Place a peanut before one of those little fellows out in the woods, and he pays no attention to it. Try your little discovery with peanuts. You will know by his reactions if it is one of our red-squirrel gang."

"OK—we do that tomorrow," said Duke. "Now there is something else here . . ." And he began fishing about in his packsack for another object he had brought back.

But Giny was tired of waiting. She did not call "dinner" again, but instead walked past us carrying a steaming platter of broiled ham. And Duke and I followed to the table as if we had been caught by hooks.

XX

MORE ABOUT MO

DUKE was on edge to get going the next morning. The fruit juice, bacon, eggs, bran muffins and coffee Giny had prepared were handled with savage Ranger tactics. Previous mornings he had insisted on helping with the dishes, over all the objections we could hurl at him. It was a novel sight—a captain doing K.P.! It gave me quite a thrill in the light of my army experience, when I was *not* a captain.

But this morning the atmosphere was charged with a sort of happy hurry and joyful excitement.

"Better skip the dishes this morning," I began, all needlessly.

"Who said anything about not skipping them?" said Duke, with a little giggle that sounded like an echo of old times. "Those dishes are all OK—good for several meals yet. I'm late for an appointment."

Even as he talked he was making ready for the day, putting his equipment in his packsack. Giny had his lunch prepared, and as usual there was a piece of apple pie included, wrapped in oiled paper.

"Don't forget to take peanuts," I cautioned. Certainly that morning I had a faculty for saying unnecessary things.

"What do you think causes this?" Duke asked, whirling about and pointing to the bulging pockets of his jacket.

Duke had enough peanuts along to feed all the red squirrels in ten acres!

He left in a hurry. I hurled after him one more bit of futile and foolish advice: "Don't forget to take a boat."

But if enthusiasm could make one walk on the water, I believe the boy would have done it that morning. More seemed at stake than just the possible finding of a red squirrel that had disappeared.

The experience lived up to highest expectations. Duke was not gone long. In about an hour I saw him coming back toward the island rowing so fast he almost left the boat behind. He landed and came running up to the cabin, his face flushed with excitement. There was more of the real Duke there that moment than we had seen at any time since his return.

"Hey, you people!" he called as he rushed in the door. "That is Mo over there, sure as you are born!"

Little by little we learned the story. The red squirrel had been found in the same oak tree lying on the same limb where Duke had seen him the day before, soaking up the morning sunshine. He had hardly moved as Duke came directly beneath him. Duke talked to him for a few minutes, and then began tossing a peanut up and catching it just as we always had done before the Squints. The tiny red squirrel made no move at first, but calmly watched the peanut as it rose toward him and fell away. Then suddenly he started, sitting up and scratching the back of his head

with his hind foot—just thinking it over, Duke said. He
looked down at the man below him, who kept talking to
him in such an appealing way. Excitement began to
grow in the little creature. He gave forth an unending
little chatter, not like the scolding noise of his kind given
when they are annoyed, but one that indicated a tremendous stir within him. He ran back and forth on the oak
limb as if he didn't know just what to do.

"I knew then it was one of our Squints," Duke said excitedly. "It was just too evident the little guy was being
stirred by memories he couldn't figure out at first."

The evidence of his identity mounted. Duke moved
over and tapped on the trunk of the tree with a peanut.
This, too, was a move often made in the early days of the
red squirrels. The tot started down the tree, his tail
twitching with nervousness, the while he kept up that
funny chatter. Duke held the peanut for him to take.
Summoning all his courage, the squirrel inched on until
his nose almost touched it. Then fear seized him, and
with squirrel shrieks the equivalent of "Help! Murder!
Thieves!—Police! Police!" he almost flew to the extreme
top of the tree.

But there was no letup in the siren persuasion from
below. *Tap, tap, tap* went the peanut on the tree trunk,
while Duke coaxed and coaxed for him to come back.
From somewhere away up in the foliage Duke could hear
the nervous and inquisitive little chatter begin again. Fear
was subsiding, and curiosity was mingling with memory.
His actions were quicker now. He came down rapidly,

but with typical squirrel caution. He ran around the tree one way, and peeked at Duke from the left. Then he ran around the other way and peeked at him from the right. Then it was left, then right, then left, then right, until Duke was dizzy from watching him. Once more he had reached the danger zone of the last three inches short of the peanut. There he hung, chattering and chattering. Duke's arm went to sleep from holding it high in one position so long. But when he tried advancing the peanut ever so little, away went the timid red squirrel to the very top of the tree again. Undoubtedly the little fellow wanted that peanut. But a terrible battle was going on inside him between the wilderness caution he had learned and memory of the days when he lived freely with human friends.

Duke decided to make the first test less severe. He forced several peanuts into crevices of the bark of the tree, and then sat down at a short distance to watch. Presently the squirrel worked his way down the tree in much the same manner as before. He peaked out from left and right, and right and left. Then the little fellow discovered the peanuts in the bark!

"You should have seen him sneak up on that peanut!" said Duke, with a moderate but genuine little chuckle. "I bet he thought he was stealing it. He stopped his chattering and moved up in silence, then suddenly grabbed the nut and ran all the way to the treetop. He went so fast I believe he slid up."

We stopped Duke there! A squirrel can go up a tree

amazingly fast, but he can't *slide* up. Duke took it back, but insisted it looked that way.

From then on there was constant progress. This was our little friend Mo, and no question about it. After he had taken half a dozen peanuts from the bark, he accepted one from Duke's fingers. This he ate at once, sitting on the long branch where he had first been seen, and dropping the crumbled bits of shell in Duke's hair. He came

back for more and more, often doing that little stunt so characteristic of him in his baby days—hanging head down on the side of the tree, holding on by his hind feet and stretching his front feet as part of a great big yawn. Within an hour he was so fearless he would touch Duke's hand, and he concluded his performance in a way that was Mo all over. He ran out on the long branch, stretched out on his tummy, legs hanging over at each side, and gave himself up to complete rest.

Later that day Giny and I went with Duke to see his great discovery. It was Mo, unquestionably! How he came there, and why, is one of those mysteries of nature that make human beings guess. But he *was* there, and he was very much at home in his new location. We accepted the facts we looked on, but the why and wherefore of it all we had to give up. And as Duke suggested, if Mo was alive and could be found, why not also Eeny, Meeny and Miney? Surely it wouldn't take much more of a miracle.

Our soldier had a question to ask that evening. This time it was not about a plant, or a creature. On an old trail marker he had found words that gripped his thought, and he had copied them in his notebook. He read them to Giny and me as we sat before the grate fire.

" 'There is no hope so bright but is the beginning of its own fulfillment,' " quoted Duke. He looked at me for a moment. "Do you believe that?"

"Yes, Duke, I do," I said, but I did not feel like enlarging on the great thought the words presented. Something more than human argument had led Emerson to make that bold, courageous statement. The truth of such a saying must be known in the heart, and is not established by debate. So we waited in silence for our soldier to say more if he cared to, or let matters stand where they were.

Now the clock *ticked* and *tocked* much louder, and there was deeper meaning in its chimes. Duke's hands were clasped and his elbows rested on his knees, while he stared into the fire with a faraway look. Presently he said simply, "I am beginning to believe it too."

XXI

WHICH WAY IS NORTH?

THERE came a day of rain, and Duke broke up his routine a bit. He decided the fish might be hungry, so he went out to "snag a few," as he said. All day long he roamed about the lake in a boat, the sky pelting him with droplets, while he lashed out with his casting, or dropped his baited hook hopefully into mysterious depths.

I wonder what makes a man do that, and like it. I have often done it myself, but I never knew why. Certainly, if a fisherman were *ordered* to sit out in such a deluge, he would be ready to start a revolution. But fishing seems to justify any inconvenience or discomfort. The number of fish caught can hardly be considered the compensation. It is seldom these days that anyone gets very many of them anywhere. But I guess it isn't fish that fishermen are after, it is just fishing. And certainly, there is plenty of that.

After ten hours of work, Duke's catch was very limited, but it was adequate for dinner. Giny prepared the fish fillets in masterly manner, rolling each piece in corn meal and cooking it in deep fat until it was golden brown. There were baked potatoes to go with it, creamed string beans and stewed tomatoes from Giny's canning of the previous summer. Then she topped the meal with blueberry pie so thick that Duke said he could have crawled between the crusts.

Duke went to bed early that night. He said he wanted to listen to the rain pattering on his tent house, but he didn't stay awake long enough to hear much of it. He was exhausted from his strenuous day of fishing.

The next morning was clear and sunny, the world sparkling with the clinging raindrops of yesterday. Duke was on the go again. This time, he said, he was going to get away from trails. He wanted to take a look at the back country, and see if he could find a little lake that I had told him was somewhere beyond Vanishing Lake. I was sure I need not worry about his getting lost. A man trained to find his way through jungles would have no trouble with the open forests of the north. He knew how to make use of a compass, and I had lent him mine. Certainly he would not be like the people who were lost so long all the rangers in the district were searching for them. When they were found they were going in exactly the wrong direction—because they thought the compass pointed back to camp. Or there was the sweet young thing who asked me how to point a compass. When I explained that you don't point it, that through magnetic influence it always points north, she said, "But what if you are not going that way?"

Duke knew that all the territory he would travel was west of our lake, and therefore if he headed east toward the close of day, he was sure to find a familiar shore or trail.

He returned all right, to bring us news of a simple adventure that set us aglow with happiness. While we worked over another good dinner drawn from Giny's endless bag of kitchen tricks, we heard the story.

Duke had left the trails near Vanishing Lake, wandering on, giving little attention to what direction he took. He came to swampland, so entangled he could not make his way through it. He skirted the fringe. There were deer to be seen in several places along his meandering route, and chipmunks and red squirrels who paid not the slightest attention to the peanuts he tossed to them. He climbed steep hills, worked along forest-covered ridges, until he came to a valley so still and beautiful he decided to have his lunch there and bide awhile. The vale was peopled with good-sized maples and hemlocks, beneath which no brush could grow. It seemed, he said, that he had accidentally found the parlor of Nature. At one point there was a newly fallen aspen tree, still bearing young leaves. Several of the branches were in such arrangement that they made a perfect chair. Here Duke sat to eat his lunch and read a little.

He had been there for perhaps an hour, and was deeply absorbed in what he was reading, when he heard a little grunting noise coming from the end of the log on which he was sitting. There stood a tremendously large, old porcupine—the largest he had ever seen, Duke said.

"Was it by any chance Salt or Pepper?" I asked.

"Much too large, as I remember them," declared Duke, and he went on to describe the startlingly friendly attitude of the animal.

"At first I thought he didn't know I was there," Duke went on. "The old fellow came up the trunk of that fallen tree, right toward me. And as he came he kept giving a call like a yawn—this way."

And Duke stretched his arms far to the tune of "Ho—ho—hmmmmm" in tones that started high and slowly descended.

Giny and I were leaning forward now, eager for the rest of the story. There were things about this old porcupine that were strangely familiar. Duke told how the creature came on up the log without the slightest evidence of fear, pausing occasionally to scratch himself in lazy fashion. Duke talked to him a bit, and moved a little—said he figured it was best to make sure the animal knew he was there.

"I didn't want him to be so surprised he would whirl around and hit me a slap with that tail of his," he said, knowing well the power and punch the old porcupine carries along behind him.

But this creature had no notion of slapping Duke. In fact, his intentions were of the friendliest nature.

"He came right up within three feet of me," said Duke with growing enthusiasm. "I didn't risk touching him, but I feel sure that I might have done so. He stayed there, too—within arm's length. He didn't want to go away."

I could hold back my excitement no longer. "Duke, tell me—how large was he? Measure it off."

Duke held his hands fully thirty inches apart. "From nose to tip of tail, he was fully that long," he declared.

"And were his quills light-colored, so that he presented a gray appearance?"

"Yes."

"And he put his feet in your lap—didn't he?"

"Yes, I was coming to that. How did you know?" asked Duke. "When I moved away a little, he kept coming after me."

"And did he sit and stare at you, looking as if he wanted to talk?"

"He certainly did, looked right at me until I felt embarrassed."

"And he didn't run away, but stayed on the log near you?"

"Never moved until I arose to go. Then he sat up, shook his quills, grunted a little and settled down again."

I looked at Giny. She had formed the same opinion I had. No porcupine in the world would behave that way with a human being—except our old-time pet, Inky! Two years had passed since we had seen him. There had been no sign of him at the salt lick where we had met so many times in previous years. I had walked the forest trails calling for him in vain. But Duke, strolling at random in the woods, had entered the valley where this patriarch of a porky had settled.

Duke was not very helpful about the location of that valley. He hadn't known which way he walked to get there, he only knew he had walked in a generally easterly direction to come back. It might have been northeast he traveled, or southeast, or just east—he didn't know. What was the valley like? Well, it was low—but all valleys are like that. There were maple and hemlock trees in it, but hundreds of such groves could be found. There was a lot of wintergreen growing on the surrounding hills, but there never is a hill without some of it. And he said there were crows flying high overhead—which, of course, was a big help.

"But you found Inky, old top," I said, "and that fulfills another hope of mine. I'm going to search for him. I don't know how I'll ever find the valley, or identify it if I do get there, but it's worth a try."

"I know how you can recognize it if you get there—by your compass."

"By compass? How would I ever know a valley by compass unless I knew exactly in which direction it lay to begin with?"

"No, I didn't say by compass—I said you could recognize the place by *your* compass."

"*My* compass?"

"Yes, I just remembered I left it there. I put it down on that aspen tree and stepped back from it to let the needle settle. I noted some tall trees that stood right east of me, and planned to walk toward them. Then I got so excited about that porcupine I just walked away without the compass. It makes it all easy. You will know the valley because your compass is there, or you can know your compass because it is in that valley."

XXII

LESSON FROM A DRAGONFLY

SOMETIMES summer sends little hot days ahead while it is still springtime—like scouts to see where the sizzling season will settle. It seems to me that never is heat felt more than on one of these prematurely torrid days. People generally think of the woods as cool. While I have never known a real warm night in the forest, there have been days that try the temper of anyone not particularly adept at hot-weather living. The forests slow down all breezes, whether hot or cold. And while one does not object if the winter winds reduce their pace and their chill, we generally like every bit a summer breeze can give. I have been on trails and portages in the forest when it seemed to me that if it went one degree hotter I would be perfectly broiled.

A south wind brought along a couple of hot days while Duke was with us, and placed them fairly in our laps. Duke chided us a little when we mentioned the heat. He said they went skating at such temperatures down in the South Pacific. But I noticed his journeys into the woods were brief those two days. He returned early enough to take a swim in the lake, the waters of which still held some of winter's chill.

But Duke couldn't keep away from problems. When he stepped into the water at the edge of the island, something struck him on the legs halfway between the ankle and the knee. Now there is nothing more difficult to endure than to encounter something alive—anything—under water. There is no way to figure out what it is, and imagination at once pictures the thing to be at least a baby sea serpent.

I remember once when I was wading in an Illinois river I stepped on an eel. It squirmed out from under my foot, only wanting to get away, but it threw me close to hysterics. I should have known what it was, having caught eels and handled them on many occasions. But I couldn't see this one, and all that I knew was that somewhere in the depths of the cloudy water was something that wiggled, squirmed and felt as big as a fire hose. I left the water so suddenly those who saw me swore there was a waterspout where I came out.

Duke had about the same sensation, and the same reaction. Something alive and very slick bumped against his shinbones. As far as he was concerned, it felt in size somewhere between a muskellunge and a submarine. Duke didn't run out. He started an Australian crawl that cut a trench through the water out about fifty yards. There he trod about calling wildly for me. I was in my bathing suit and went running, afraid something had happened to him.

"There is a low-down alligator right here by the shore, and the so-and-so bit me!" he yelled.

"Nothing bit you but your imagination," I said, without the least bit of sympathy. I knew there were no alligators in our lake unless nature had gone completely crazy, and, better still, there were no eels there! So, glad to appear brave before a soldier, I stepped boldly into the water and began wading out. I had taken only a few steps to where I was waist deep, when *something* struck me about the knees. It was alive, slick and it wiggled! Immediately I joined Duke. I think I even beat his time just a little. There we both trod water, yelling for Giny.

Giny refused to be excited. "You're just trying to frighten me," she said, and added, "You are not going to do it." She was ready for a swim, too, and sat on the little pier we had built there, letting her feet get accustomed to the water. Suddenly she let out a screech, and jerked her feet up on the pier. Something alive and slick had struck her feet.

Duke and I swam in. The unseen demon struck us both as we were wading.

"I never had anything that doesn't hurt at all hurt as much as that thing does!" giggled Duke as he climbed up on the little pier. There the three of us stared into waters that didn't reveal a thing. Duke wished he had a depth bomb.

But as the water quieted down from the disturbance we had made, I discovered the very harmless cause of all this excitement. Very near shore I saw a little swirling motion. Looking more closely I could see a small fish, a rock bass, just under the surface in the shallows, its tail fan-

ning slowly back and forth. Beneath it in among some
pebbles was the cause of its great concern. There was a
deposit of eggs. To hatch them, the fish must keep the
water about them in circulation constantly. I had known
of the ferocity of largemouth bass at spawning time, but
never had I seen this little fellow carry on that way. We
tested the creature, now that we had made the discovery
which removed our fear. Duke stuck his foot in the
water, and instantly the pugnacious fish darted for it.
It could not bite, but it certainly hit hard, striking again
and again.

"Come on!" said Giny, leading the way down the shore.
"It won't hurt us one bit to let that nursery alone and go
swimming someplace else."

Duke hadn't gone far, though, until something else
caught his attention. "Hey, what's going on here?" he
called. "What kind of a contraption is this?"

He was kneeling beside a hemlock tree, watching a
beetlelike creature climbing up the bark. Duke had seen
him come out of the water, crawl across a bit of ground
and then start up the tree.

"If you have had enough of a swim, let's watch him,
Duke," I said, noting what it was. "You'll see something
mighty interesting."

Duke had come upon a dragonfly, in its larva stage. We
hurriedly slipped on robes, obtained a watch and magnifying glass, and returned to observe one event in the life
of this strange little insect.

Nearly everyone who has ever been out under open

skies has seen the dragonfly darting through the air at great speed, zooming up and diving like an airplane. He certainly needs no wing training or practice. He is an expert flier from the first. He joins hundreds of thousands of his kind in their great industry—eating mosquitoes, gnats and almost any other bug smaller than he. For his size he is one of the most savage creatures in all nature. Seen through a magnifying glass, his face is absolutely terrifying. He looks like the kind of creature we see in nightmares. His appetite is amazing. He eats and eats. One of these insects has been known to take a good bite out of himself and eat it down with relish. A naturalist once kept one from feeding normally for only a few minutes. Then he turned the tail of the creature so that it came before the insect's mouth. Promptly he took a bite, and then a second one, before his self-inflicted wounds got the better of him. When he is at the most conspicuous stage of his life, he is equipped with double wings that make him a marvel at flying. But there is a long period during which he is not seen, unless by some nature observer who has gone to a great deal of preparation.

While in a canoe one evening, we saw a dragonfly of this type sail along trailing a long egg sac. It dipped sharply down near us, to a place where a small stump protruded above the surface of the water. With a quick circular movement, it flew around the stump, wrapping the egg sac about it, and then breaking free, it darted away.

The eggs so deposited would drift to the bottom of the

shallow water. In time they would hatch, and out of them develop the kind of a creature we now saw before us on the tree. But it would be a long time before the insect emerged from his lake home—perhaps three years. Then in a relatively short time he would develop into the dragonfly as he is generally known.

Duke and I watched the entire metamorphosis that afternoon, made notes of it and timed it. It was hard to believe that the dull and rather unattractive beetlelike creature before us would ever evolve into a beautiful winged insect. But even as we spoke of this, the change began. He commenced expanding, growing, developing about the head and shoulders. The legs on which he had crawled out of the water were rigid with stiff little claws firmly fixed in the bark of the tree, while the head pointed upward. Then the old shell began to split down the back, and the new form of the creature came "boiling out," as Duke said. It bent over backward, until the new head touched the old tail. There it hung for many minutes, while internal processes of growth took place. Duke and I looked at the odd creature through our magnifying glass. We noted pulsing action about the throat and in the abdomen. Two white threads still bound him to the old shell, supporting him while his orderly evolution took place.

"Duke," said I, "do you realize what a startling change is coming into the life of this little insect? He didn't see much of the world during the three years he lived at the bottom of this lake. He fed on tiny organisms. All about him was darkness and gloom. He was like people who let themselves dwell in the depths of selfish thinking. But now he is going to have wings. He is going to rise up and really see things."

"I guess he hears what you are saying," commented Duke. "Look at him struggle to get free of that old skeleton."

It was as Duke said. There was increased animation about the insect. His new feet and legs were ready for use, and he was anxious to use them. He pulled his newly formed body upward until he faced in the same direction as his old shell. Then taking firm hold with his new feet, he began twisting, turning, struggling to be free. He was actually violent in his efforts. The holding cords snapped. He pulled the lower end of his body out of the old shell, which looked like a shoe he had outgrown. Then he established himself firmly right beside his old "home." Already he was longer than this shell and it was difficult to see how he had ever fitted into it. And now he stood free on the threshold of a new life.

"Wouldn't it be grand if we could climb out of some of our mental shells that way?" Duke was saying. "Boy, if we could leave our sorrows, our regrets, our envies and hatreds like that—what a world we would see!"

"Right, Duke!" It was fine to see this boy thinking his way through. "And experience shows that people can climb out of those old skeletons when they try. We don't have to drag along these worn-out garments of our old ways of thinking if we do not want to. But here comes a miracle of growth—watch those wings!"

The wings had looked like crumpled bits of paper down the insect's back. But suddenly they started to grow at an amazing rate. They had been about half the length of the body to begin with, shapeless and wrinkled. Even as we watched, they stretched out, losing their wrinkles and becoming winglike in appearance.

"That took exactly fifteen minutes," said Duke, who had been timing the event.

Next the wings were dormant for a few minutes while the body took up the growth. It was in well-marked segments, and these began to expand "like an accordion," as Duke suggested. In thirty minutes the body was longer than the wings, and a quarter-inch thick. The insect now was three times as long as the old skeleton, which still stood beside him, its lifeless feet clinging desperately to the bark of the tree.

Now there was more action in the wings. As yet they were lengthwise over the back, but they would not stay in that position long. They began moving a little as the insect discovered he had the strength to operate them. Then suddenly, at a single move, he raised the wings until they were at right angles to his body. Here they were ready for flying. Never again would they come to position over his back. He resembled now the fast-flying types of airplane. In substance, the wings were marvelously delicate and beautiful. They were perfectly trans-

parent, and were constantly reflecting little darts of light
from the sun.

"Watch every move closely now, Duke," I said, though
the captain was so taken with this drama of nature he
really needed no such caution. "The miracle is almost
completed. Look at those wings vibrate."

A little fluttering had developed in the wings. Faster
and faster they went, until suddenly the creature took to
the air.

"One hour and forty-seven minutes since we first saw
him," cried Duke, "and look at that rascal go!"

Duke had picked up the abandoned shell, and was crum-
bling it between his fingers. He looked very thoughtful.

"Do you know, Duke, I wonder if it isn't that way with
us," I said. "The insect pulled out of an old skeleton,

left it behind and went flying away to a greater way of living. If nature so takes care of his future, it seems certain that it will look after us in some such manner, too."

Duke had looked up at me sharply, surprised. "I was just thinking the very same things!" he said, and he added quickly, "But you are a naturalist. Do you find it possible in the light of your science to believe that life goes on—beyond?"

"Duke," I said seriously, "there is nothing in all the realm of nature that takes issue with the thought of eternal life. In nature we never see the beginning of anything and we never see the finish of it. There is something in our very hearts that tells us life is of that order, without beginning or end. And remember—'There is no hope so bright but is the beginning of its own fulfillment.' "

But Duke was not hearing me now. His eyes had taken on the faraway look we had seen several times during his stay. He turned his head slightly and looked toward the west where a salmon-pink cloud hung like a scarf with which the day was waving farewell. His lips quivered a little, his eyes moistened, and so softly that I could barely hear the words, he whispered:

"The rascal!"

XXIII

A BELIEVE-IT-OR-NOT DAY

DUKE'S leave was slipping by. In one way it seemed to fly, in another it was timeless. The hours that had gone were as if they had had no duration at all, and the hours to come looked all too few. But there were gratifying changes in our soldier. Not all that we hoped for had developed as yet. He was of good cheer, his nervousness was vanishing, he was intensely interested in the forest world about him. But we had not yet seen him rise to one of those peaks of happiness we had known in earlier years. In other words, there were no cackle spasms. He laughed slightly, and was ready of wit, but it was all too moderate for our Duke. Then, too, we could see there was still a dread of returning. One night when conversation was forced into a channel that brought mention of his leaving, the smile faded instantly from his face, his eyes narrowed, and he pressed his lips together.

"Still dread it so much, my boy?" I asked, patting him on the shoulder.

"I guess I do," he said, as if half ashamed. "I wish I didn't, for it has to be done. Oh, when the time comes, I'll do it all right—but now it sickens me."

"I feel sure you'll be ready, Duke—more ready than you believe," I assured him.

177

The next morning Duke suggested a little canoeing. The day was perfect for it. Not a breeze was stirring, and the waters were so still the surrounding earth and sky lived again in their mirrored depths. Giny had her day planned, but it didn't take me long to convince myself I needed a vacation from my typewriter. So Duke and I started out on a canoe trip that was long and filled with adventures which still have us puzzled.

As we circled the north shore of our little lake, we discovered a deer near the foot of a young maple tree that had been uprooted probably by a storm. The tree had not fallen all the way to the ground, but had struck a pine with its top branches and lodged there. Half fallen, it sloped at rather a mild angle. The deer, a beautiful doe about three years old, had been feeding on the young leaves, and apparently found them much to her liking. She was so involved in her browsing that she paid no attention to us as we drifted in quite close. We reached a point where we could almost touch her with our paddles, and there we rested in silence.

The doe was having a desperate time to reach the luscious leaves. She stretched her neck as far as she could, then reared on her hind legs to reach farther. Still the best and most of this delectable dinner was just beyond her. Then the impossible happened. The doe climbed the tree!

Of course, when we speak of tree-climbing, we generally think of a long stretch of tree trunk, and the climber getting a strangle hold on it while he shins his way upward. The deer didn't do *that!* This tree was slanting, and its lower limbs were not far from the ground. A man with an exceptionally good sense of balance could have walked up the trunk. The deer climbed until it was ten or twelve feet from the ground. It felt its way timidly up the sloping trunk, caught its little front hoofs in the lower branches, always reaching its head forward to nip off the next and the next young leaf. We dared not laugh, for fear we would frighten the animal and cause it to fall. Because of this, I sculled the canoe around a point of land where we couldn't be seen, and ran its bow in the sand.

"Now, Duke," I said, "I want you to tell me what you just saw. And if it doesn't check up, then I don't want to go back to Giny. I wouldn't want her to have to take care of me."

"No," said Duke, "you tell me what *you* saw—and if it isn't right then I don't dare go back to the Army."

"Well—let's both say it at the same time," I suggested. "Are you ready?"

He was ready.

"Then begin!"

And in unison we said the words in the same meter with which a child reads out of its first storybook:

"I—saw—a—deer—climb—a—tree!"

Then it must be true. People don't dream the same dream. And besides, we could hear the animal now, running off through the woods, snorting back at whoever had disturbed her tossed-salad luncheon.

Duke and I landed at the fallen maple to look the place over. We climbed the tree and found it not difficult to go up on hands and knees. Scratches made by the sharp hoofs of the doe were plainly in evidence. Bark was nipped off the low limbs. Leaves had been bitten off the branches as far as the creature could reach.

"All right," said Duke, "we saw a deer climb a tree! But we had better never say anything about it. We never had insanity in our family, but how will people know that? Raise your right hand and swear—never a word about this!"

And never a word was said—until we got home that night. Then we had to tell Giny of this adventure, and also of some other things that happened later.

We had paddled on beyond the creek mouth, and drifted there for a few moments observing the swallows dart and dive in their insect feeding. There we flushed a small flock of ducks, and watched them beat the water with their wings as they rose in a swift graceful flight.

"Look at the eagle, Duke," I exclaimed, pointing to an old dead tree on a distant shore, where one of the great birds perched at the very top. Duke didn't see him at first. I pointed more strenuously. "You must see him quickly," I insisted, as if Duke weren't doing his best. "That fellow will see us in a moment and head away. They never like to be close to human beings."

"Now I have found him!" Duke exclaimed. "And look, he is taking off."

True, the great bird was leaving his perch. He spread

his tremendous wings—like a B-29, Duke suggested—and gracefully took to the air, but not in the direction I had expected. Instead of seeking the safety of distance, he glided right toward us. Duke and I froze in our positions. The eagle dipped close to the water, and came on.

"He's going to take off my hat!" whispered Duke, some true concern mixed in with his humor. "Should I duck?"

"If you get hit by an eagle you will be the first man who ever did," I whispered back. "You want to be original, don't you? Sit still!"

That mammoth bird passed within twenty feet of the bow of our canoe, and not fifteen feet above the water. He looked squarely at us when he passed, and Duke insisted he saluted, but I didn't see that. Certainly I had never seen an eagle do such a thing before. Why he did it, I do not know. Beyond question he saw us. Then he simply glided on to the other side of the lake, and lighted at the top of a tall tree.

"Let's put it in with the other adventure we aren't going to tell," suggested Duke. "This is getting me shaky. Maybe we don't live right."

We were at the narrows of the lake now, where it was easy to see each shore. On one side the brush was thick at the water's edge so that one could not look deeply into the woods. But the other shore was coated with a magnificent stand of virgin pines, in which there was very little underbrush, and we could see far back among the stately, beautiful bodies of the great trees.

Duke had been looking toward the pine-covered shore

for a few moments, and then he asked, in tones that seemed timid, "Have you ever seen a duck walk on stilts?"

"What was that, Duke?"

"I say, have you ever seen a duck walk on stilts?"

"Now, now, old boy, take it easy," I said. "Don't let this day get you down. No, a duck doesn't walk on stilts!"

"Then what is that I see over in the woods?" he asked, pointing with his paddle.

I looked over—and saw Duke's duck walking on stilts. It was one of the most amusing sights I have ever looked on—and this was the only time I ever saw it. A great blue heron strutted along through the woods apparently enjoying a morning stroll. Now a blue heron does not do that, any more than deer climb trees and eagles fly up saluting! A heron has long legs so he can wade in the water, and there is where he uses them. Otherwise, he flies from place to place. But walking in the woods—it just isn't done in the best heron society. Nevertheless, here went the old creature, as if he were on parade. A heron's legs are put on sort of backward, anyway. His knee doesn't bend like ours, and I am sure we must be made right. It folds to the back, so that his lower leg from the knee down comes up forward of him. I suppose it is a good idea to have it so for walking through water, when he must always be reaching far ahead for his next step. But it certainly looks funny operating like that for a walk in the woods. Besides, this heron's long neck went far forward and back again like a bobbin with each step.

The whole thing defies description. I guess the only

way you can know what a blue heron looks like walking through the woods is to see one doing it! Certainly, Duke and I will never forget the sight of the great bird working those long, spindle legs bent in the wrong direction, selecting each step as if it were a life-and-death decision, and his long head and neck going out and in like a piston with no place to go.

"Let's paddle home blindfolded," suggested Duke. "I don't believe I can take any more."

But our day and our adventures were far from over. We circled about and went up a little creek that winds back into rather wild country. Here the white-throated sparrows were singing, and kingbirds zoomed out to catch luckless insects. An animal started up in the tall grass at the stream side, and we could follow his flight back toward the forest by the commotion of the grass and brush. We did not see it, though it may well have been a bear.

Then Duke discovered a duck on the water a few feet ahead of the canoe. It began putting up a desperate struggle.

"It's been hurt," declared Duke. "The wing seems to have been broken. Move me up a little, and maybe I can catch it."

I steered the canoe toward the frightened bird, and moved forward until we were almost within reach. Duke reached out to grasp it, but it made a terrific effort and managed to fly a few feet ahead. Again we glided toward it, for a bird in that condition would have no chance of surviving even one night in the forest. Once more we reached a point where Duke might have caught the duck, had it not repeated its flight for a few feet more. We followed. Sooner or later it must tire. Perhaps we could set the broken wing, protect the duck for a few days while it mended, and then release it. But it fought against capture desperately with all its strength. Time and again Duke would get within reach, but it would assemble strength enough for still another flight.

During this period we had gone a considerable distance from the place where we had first seen it. The duck sat on the water, looking at us rather calmly now. Thinking it was exhausted at last, we moved once more toward it. This time, without waiting for us to come very near, the deceitful old creature rose from the water in perfect flight, its wings in excellent condition! It circled high over the treetops and, doubling back of us, dropped out of sight somewhere in the creek in the direction from which we had come.

Duke was dumfounded. I was just dumb.

"Of all things, to let that scamp put this over on me after my many years in the woods," I was grumbling at myself.

"Put what over on whom?" Duke asked, still uncertain what had happened. "Did that wing suddenly get well?"

"No, it was never even sick!" I said, a bit chagrined. "Come on back—I think we'll see what dupes we have been."

We went back around several bends in the creek until we were in view of the water where we had first seen the

duck. Things were just as I had suspected. There was
our "crippled" bird paddling away as fast as it could,
followed by seven or eight baby ducks who might have
been on their first swim. The mother likely had run them
into hiding at our approach and then put on this act of
being crippled just to draw us away from them. When
she had taken us far enough to feel safe, she abandoned
her deceit, flew back to her babies who were possibly
hidden under shore grass, and escorted them away.

I was still impatient with myself. "Duke, I have seen
that done scores of times, and still I fall for it. Those
birds are such good actors, they make you believe it is
real."

"I'm glad you didn't expose the hoax," was Duke's
comment. "It wouldn't have been half as much fun if you
had."

But our *believe-it-or-not day* had one more feature
left. Our lake is one of a chain of twenty-eight lakes having navigable thoroughfares, and canoeing is unlimited.
It was late afternoon when we headed toward home once
more. As we approached a pier near a neighbor's cabin,
we noted a creature running out all the way to the end of
it. I reasoned it must be a dog, though even from a distance it did not look like one, and no dog was supposed to
be at that place at that time anyway. The animal drew
gasps from both Duke and me when it deliberately dived
off the pier into deep water. When it came to the surface,
it swam about with obvious pleasure. We kept on paddling
toward it, fascinated by the way it enjoyed itself in the

water. A schoolboy playing hooky on a hot day, and going to the old swimming hole, couldn't have had a better time. But our surprise had just begun. Having finished his dip, the animal swam back to the end of the pier, which was about two feet above the water. Lunging upward, it caught the end board with its front feet—and pulled itself right out of the water up on that pier!

Now dogs have been known to count, to spell, to find their master's slippers, to carry the mail, and go fetch almost anything they are sent for—but they can't chin themselves on the end of a pier!

"That's going too far!" said Duke. "I quit! Just get me out of this—that's all I ask. Dogs don't do **that**. Where is the nearest psychiatrist?"

"Wait a minute, Duke!" I exclaimed. "You haven't seen anything yet. That isn't a dog, it's a wildcat!"

Sure enough it was. We were rather close now, and we noticed the animal did not shake itself all over the way a dog would; it merely shook each foot in cat fashion.

Then as it moved along the pier we could see the bobtail, the sharp ears and the typical whiskers. Suddenly it discovered us, and I doubt if I have ever seen a living thing move so quickly or so gracefully before. In several marvelous leaps it cleared the remaining distance on the pier, and was off into the woods. There it vanished as if the ground had opened and taken it in.

"I know dogs don't do that," Duke was saying desperately, "but is it any better for a wildcat to take a swim and chin itself on a pier? They're all nuts—or am I?"

"Never saw such a thing before, Duke, never!" I agreed. "Cats are supposed to dread water. But that fellow did it just to have fun. Thanks again for being along. Otherwise I'd get out my Napoleon suit and give myself up. Let's go home and drink coffee."

Since then I have told this story to many woodsmen and nature students. They look at me with friendly and tolerant smiles, but they don't believe me. Or else they tell some tall tale by way of competition.

Giny was nice about it all. She was sure we wouldn't make up stories, she said. Besides, she had something to tell us out of her own experience. Duke and I braced ourselves.

"It isn't so startling," said Giny happily. "I have found Eeny! That is all. She was over at Lonestone Point. She went through the same excitement you noticed with Mo. And she took peanuts right from my hand. We have three of the five Squints located now. Are you glad?"

Glad! Certainly we were, and not only because another one of our pets had been located.

"This is the first sane thing that has happened all day long, the first thing we can prove," declared Duke. "A deer climbing a tree, an eagle saluting me, a heron taking a walk in the woods, a lame duck making a couple of monkeys out of us, and a wildcat taking a swim—and now Eeny is back. Boy, oh boy—what a day!"

Duke didn't let the sun get very high the next morning before he was over to see his favorite red squirrel.

XXIV

WHATZIT?

SOMETIMES I wish I could get a look behind the scenes
on the other side of some of our forest adventures. Always our conclusions and descriptions must be from our
human viewpoint.

Do you suppose Eeny and Mo ever had yearnings for
the human companions they once knew? Of course, such
longings would have been of lesser influence than the instincts which led them to go forth into the world, out and
beyond, else they would never have left the island. But
I think we have reason to believe such desires were within
their hearts. Their extreme excitement when they first
saw us after our long separation showed there was some
longing or cherished memory that the meeting gratified.

Then, too, we may be sure their mental life is somewhat
similar to our own. For, after all, we residents of this
earth are made of the same substance.

I imagine a considerable stir was afoot in the little
minds of two other red squirrels that came out to greet
us rather noisily one dawn. Their chosen country was
Point Trail's End to the west of our island, lying at much
greater distance from us than the points occupied by
Eeny and Mo. It was a beautiful daybreak they looked

on—that is if they stopped chasing each other long enough
to see it. Mackerel clouds filled the eastern sky, and the
rising sun lavished its red hues upon them. The color
rose to the zenith, lighted the horizons. The lake, with
not a single wrinkle of a wave to mar its placid face, mirrored the exquisite display above it, while tiny curls of
vapor arose from the waters to add a touch of mystery.
Birds looked on this glory and sang until it seemed their
throats could not stand the strain.

From the moment the world began to shed its night
robes and don the light of day, the two squirrels had been
afoot. Their incessant chatter sounded as if they were
staging the battle of the century. Over the ground, around
tree trunks, through foliage they raced, one pursuing
the other as if he would rip him to pieces if he ever
closed that last three feet of distance. The gap remained,
and the pursuer did not catch the pursued. Whether the
two diminutive creatures were quarreling, or if this were
a kind of sport, was a secret they carried along with them.
There couldn't have been anything so very ill-humored
about it, for occasionally they would stop and rest, perhaps only six feet apart. When both were ready, the chase
would begin again.

So noisy were the two squirrels that they attracted the
attention of the one human being who was out to see the
coming of the dawn. Duke, wanting to get as much as
possible out of his last two days at the Sanctuary, had risen
while it was yet dark and launched out in the canoe. He
was near this point when the red-squirrel rumpus began.

And he drifted close in to the shore, watching the dawn unfold in the east, and at the same time keeping track of the excitement on shore.

I knew what Duke thought as he watched the two animals and why his heart pounded a little faster as a question came into his mind. He could tell me this, and did so later. But I wonder what went through the minds of those little creatures in the moment when they had paused in a tree that overhung the water, and looked down on the drifting canoe and its occupant. Did the tall young man with dark curly hair, kindly face and eyes that flashed with excited interest look familiar to them? Did they feel a little quickening of the pulse and dig up old memories that had been stored away in half-forgotten corners of their hearts? Did they, too, question: Is it *he?*

How could they know for sure? Certainly it looked like *him.* But then these human beings are much alike, and they are always changing their skins from one color to another. Still, this one did look and act in a way that was familiar. Even if human beings look pretty much alike, they don't act alike. And this one was already showing a certain attitude of kindness similar to something they had once loved.

Anyway, why was he acting so strangely? Other human beings would look up at them, make a remark or two in a tongue they didn't understand, and pass on. But this one plainly was excited. He was making a little clucking noise, different from the sounds generally given by the two-legged creatures. Also, he was climbing out of the floating log in which he had been riding, and was walking toward the tree in which they still stayed. His face was alight with interest and excitement, but there was no threat in his attitude. Hadn't they seen just such a creature do this before—'way back in their remote childhood, nearly a year ago? Could it be that this was the human being who had fed them when their mother failed to return? Surely, that was the way he looked, and that friendly expression now so clear on his face was like the one they had seen from their improvised nest. But how could they be sure?

They chattered in soft voice to each other as the idea grew on them. It looked like *him,* it acted like *him!* Yet, maybe it wasn't! And away they went to the very top of the tree!

From their high perch, they scolded the whole world that had so much deceit in it. Better not have anything to do with a race like human beings, some of whom can be kind while others can be cruel and kill just for amusement!

But the man on the ground below would not let them alone. That clucking noise came again. He was calling them names that sounded remotely familiar. Maybe they had better take another close look, but it was just as well to be cautious. They would pull the old red-squirrel stunt of staying on the far side of the tree trunk and just peeking around at him—quickly! Don't give him a chance to draw a bead on you! Just look and then run!

And so the two of them came down the tree, whimpering and whimpering, increasing their alertness and caution as they neared the man.

But now what was this fellow doing? What was that he was tossing up in the air? Was it a stone he was throwing at them? No, he wasn't trying to hit them, just attracting their attention, and he succeeded well. That thing he was tossing up—wasn't it the kind of nut they had known when they were babies? It had been found on the island where they spent their childhood, and they hadn't found it since. Boy, but it was good—remember? Probably they mentioned the squirrel equivalent for the "biscuits that mother used to make." They had often said they would trade a bushel of acorns and pine cones for half a dozen of those things.

How they wished they might catch the one he was

handling now! Their eyes followed it as it rose and fell. But come to think of it, wouldn't that sort of prove that this was the human being they once knew? Other people had come beneath their trees, going by in fishing boats, but they hadn't tossed any of those nuts up in the air. Maybe the miracle had happened, and this man they remembered as a friend had managed to get through the winter alive! They couldn't understand why he had, though—he didn't store up any food that they could see, hadn't made a home in a tree and lined it with cedar bark, hadn't grown thicker hair to meet the cold.

But funny things happen in this world! They would test him, anyway. They would go close watching him all the time, and then while still far enough off so he could not reach them, scamper high in the trees. This they would repeat until, if he were the wrong kind, he would get discouraged and go away.

The man did not go away. He coaxed and coaxed them to come, and he kept calling those names. What was it he said?—Meeny and Miney? Say, that was it—*the very sounds the island human beings used in calling them when those nuts were being showered about on the ground!* It must be *he!* Guess they had better take the chance!

The man was holding a nut toward them now. "Dare you to take it," maybe one said to the other. "I never take a dare," said the other perhaps, and so he snatched it and ran. Hurrah! It was one of those old-time nuts, and just as good as ever!

There could be no doubt of it now. Peanuts proved this

was their childhood friend, the big fellow with the enormous but kindly hands, the one who used to laugh so much. Come on, let's get us another peanut! Certainly it's safe—and kind of good to see this creature again!

From Duke's standpoint, he knew he had found the last two of the Squints. When he drifted along the shore and saw two very small chickarees racing about, he gave immediate attention to them—for there was a certain hope in his heart. Besides, Duke felt sure there could be only one red squirrel as saucy and quarrelsome as he who was doing the chasing—it would have to be Meeny. Then when he came beneath the tree in which they had paused, there was that little chattering note of excitement which had been so obvious in Eeny and Mo when they were found.

He decided to try the peanut test. That would prove it conclusively. So for an hour he stood beneath the tree, looking up until he had a pain in the neck, coaxing and coaxing. At last Meeny—wise and tough old Meeny—came and took a peanut from his fingers! A moment later, Miney came for the offering. There could be no question about it—*these were the last two Squints!* Duke dropped several handfuls of peanuts on the ground, and hurried home to tell us the news—and to get some breakfast.

"I've got 'em! I've got 'em!" he announced excitedly as he came to the cabin.

"Yes, I know, Duke," I said as I met him at the door. "You've got 'em—but why tell the world about it?"

"No—I don't mean that. I've got Meeny and Miney.

They are over at Point Trail's End. I gave them the peanut test, and they are our Squints."

We had to go and see. Breakfast was eaten at high speed. Then Giny, Duke and I headed for the land of Meeny and Miney—going in two canoes, as Duke planned to stay on.

A little search was necessary to find the two squirrels. They were resting from their strenuous morning. The peanuts Duke had left on the ground were gone. But by persistently calling their names, and tapping with a peanut on the tree where Duke had seen them earlier, we finally stirred them up. Meeny was in the tree, and we discovered the little rascal peering down at us from high in the foliage. Miney came running over the tree-branch road a few moments later. They had to conquer fear once more, now that there were several of us. But before many minutes had passed, our old-time red-squirrel pals were taking peanut after peanut from our outstretched hands!

They would not permit us to touch them. The wilderness had entered their ways too much for that. And while we would have liked to pick them up and wool them around as we used to, it was better this way. There was something particularly attractive in the way they clung to wilderness caution, yet bridged it sufficiently to come to our finger tips. Something said, "Thus far and no farther," and we liked this feeling of their remaining in their world while we remained in ours, yet each of us free enough of fear to shake hands.

"Boy, oh boy—that's swell!" said Duke of the whole

adventure. The forest world had revealed our little friends to us once more, and there was joy in our hearts.

Duke had the *Whatzits* as we walked through the woods together for a few minutes before Giny and I returned to work at the cabin. One thing after another he pointed to with the simple question, *"Whatzit?"*

He asked the question when indicating the sweet fern. I named it for him, and showed him how to identify it by the shape of its leaves, and its very woody stem. Then I had him crumple its leaves in his fingers and note the mint odor that came from it. This is the plant preferred in making a smudge for driving mosquitoes from a tent— for its scent is pleasant to us, and not liked by the tiny insects.

"Whatzit?"

This time he pointed to a growth on the side of a dead tree. It was the shelf fungus, which lives on and amid decaying wood. Sometimes these odd and attractive plants are highly colored, giving a decorative effect to the forest.

Whatzit? Whatzit? Whatzit? Duke was boiling over with questions. We identified many things for him. There was the skunk cabbage growing low to the ground with its compact mass of insignificant flowers, giving out its skunklike odor when bruised. There was the moosewood, with its zigzag twigs, a shrub from which Indians obtained long strips of bark to lace their birchbark canoes and perform the function of rope and string. There was the Indian turnip, or jack-in-the-pulpit, with its strange little concealed flower that suggests a tiny pulpit with "Jack" delivering the sermons. And there were the dainty little fairy trumpets decorating decaying logs and stumps, sharing their world with fern moss and lichens.

It was only when we stood at the canoes, Giny and I to return to the cabin and Duke to continue in the forest, that we discovered no one had thought of Duke's lunch. Meeny and Miney had produced too much excitement. But Duke decided he would go on without it. He figured it would increase his appetite to go without lunch, and he warned Giny she had better nail the tablecloth down at dinnertime or he might eat it along with the food.

"What would you do," he asked, "if you were caught in the woods without food?"

"It would be tough right now at this season," I replied. "No berries are ripe as yet. Better not try mushrooms, unless you are sure you know them. You could eat some of those young fern leaves; the Indians did. The inner bark of the birch tree has some nourishment in it, if you can stand the taste. You could catch a fish and eat it raw. Or you could locate an old porcupine, hit him across the nose, and dine on him. . . ."

"That's enough," said Duke emphatically. "I'll wait until I get home, if you please."

Duke came home a bit earlier than we had expected. I wasn't surprised, for this business of going without lunch is not so much fun in the forest. But he had the funniest expression. It was what might be described as a long face, and yet not in the sense of being gloomy. It was simply long, his lower jaw pulled down, his lips apart, and his cheeks drawn.

"Welcome, old top!" I called to him as he approached the cabin. "Aren't you a bit ahead of yourself?"

His reply simply cannot be described. He said something, but it had less resemblance to words than any sound I have ever heard a man make. Have you ever heard a sink that has been stopped up suddenly start to gurgle? Well, that is something like it. And along with this was another noise like that a man would make if a grasshopper were hopping down his throat. If I were to spell the sounds, it would have to be:

"Bllbt! Bllbt! Har-r-r-r! Har-r-r-r-r! Bllbt!"

And Duke looked for all the world as if he were trying to talk with an egg in his mouth—an ostrich egg at that.

"What on earth has happened to you, fellow?" I exclaimed, going to him. Giny came from her dinner-making, much concerned.

There was a smile in Duke's eyes as he repeated his curious noises, and certainly he couldn't smile anywhere else then.

Giny was a little impatient with me when I started to laugh. But I knew what had happened, and I knew Duke was not in serious trouble. With deliberation, I took a pencil and a pad of paper from my desk and handed them to him.

"Now, my boy, I think I understand this," I said, when

I could hold the laughs down. "If what I think is true, you are not going to talk or eat for several hours. Tell me, Captain Duke, did you by any chance get hungry and eat some Indian turnip?"

"Bllbt! Bllbt! Har-r-r-r-r . . ." he began.

"No use, Duke," I said. "Just write it, please."

He wrote the simple words, "Yes, I tried to."

"That is what I thought, you monkey. But please tell me quickly that you did not swallow any of it."

"Couldn't," was the written reply.

Duke had played a trick on himself that has been used by practical jokers in the woods for years. The Indian turnip is not poisonous, but it has a peculiar effect on the tongue and cheeks when it is chewed. The tongue will pucker and swell until it fills the whole mouth. Many a tenderfoot has come north with a party of his pals on his first fishing trip, to find them most generous in offering him a bite of a rare Indian plant they have found. It is something extra-special! But as he chews, he feels a very odd sensation in his mouth. His tongue is tingling and swelling, his cheeks puckering. Presently his tongue is so large he can neither talk nor swallow Then his dear pals gather about him to call him names and ask him why he does not talk back. After a few hours the swelling leaves the tongue. Then the tenderfoot tells his comrades what he thinks of friends who would treat him like that— and he secretly plans the day when he can do the same to some other innocent.

Going without lunch had not been easy for Duke, we

learned through much writing. He had wanted food. He tried the inner bark of a birch tree, but said he would rather eat rubber. Ferns weren't so good either. He saw a porky, but certainly didn't relish him! Then he spied the plant I had identified as Indian turnip. He had always liked turnips, cooked or raw, and so he dug one of this woods variety, washed it in Vanishing Lake, and began chewing on the woody fiber. He said his tongue puffed up like a balloon tire, and he figured he had better come home and find if there was any way of deflating it.

We threatened to eat our dinner while Duke looked on in helplessness. But we couldn't do that. Giny placed the food in the oven, while we reduced the size of Duke's tongue. Gradually his words became more distinct, and at last he sat at the table and ate as much as three men generally do.

"I never knew how important a tongue is," Duke declared. "Believe me, I am going to be careful how I use mine from now on."

XXV

"URCH"

OPPORTUNITY and experience both knocked at our door the next morning. Giny and I were at the cabin at the time, busy with the multitude of things which constantly stand before us. Duke had departed for his rendezvous with nature—giving us his solemn promise that he would not dine on Indian turnip again.

There came just one sharp knock against the glass in our front door. Giny and I were on our feet instantly. We hastened to the door, threw it wide open and looked about on the ground. At first nothing that would explain the sound could be found. We thought it might be a pine cone, but cones were not falling from trees so early in the season, and squirrels were not yet cutting them down. It might have been a limb broken from a tree, but there was no such stick lying around.

Then we discovered the cause, and a pitiful little cause it was. In a shadow lay a nestling song sparrow, his beak open, his eyes closed, while his immature wings quivered as if life were leaving him. He was a pathetic picture, so small and helpless. No doubt he had made a flight from his nest a bit too early. His experience and control of flight were not equal to the hazards of the world. Trees

he could dodge easily, but when it came to a door with glass in it, he was confronted with something he did not understand. Likely he had headed as best he could for what he thought was an opening. The door reflected the image of the sky to him. Into the glass he had crashed, perhaps in his thought making a head-on collision with another baby song sparrow that looked and flew just exactly like himself.

"Poor little urchin!" Giny exclaimed, as she gently gathered him in her hands. He looked the part. His feather clothes were much bedraggled and didn't fit him very well. His head was bare, and he had no tail feathers at all. No wonder he couldn't steer straight. His wings and feet looked too large for the rest of him, and all in all it seemed as if he were made up of extra parts that didn't match.

Had he fallen into the hands of almost anyone except Giny, his earthly life might have ended right there. But as we have seen often before, Giny doesn't give up readily.

"Come on, Urch," she was saying, "we won't let this get us down. You have a lot of singing to do in this world."

She had carried the little fellow into the cabin and was holding him in her cupped hands to keep him warm. He raised his frail head as if making an effort to respond to her appeal, but it was too heavy and it dropped again. His eyes were now almost closed, and he gasped as if each breath might be his last.

"Urch, Urch, you can do it!" cried Giny. "Here, let me help you breathe."

Taking his beak between her lips, she breathed gently, forcing the air right down his throat. This continued for ten or fifteen seconds, when suddenly the little creature shook himself and straightened up. His eyes came open and he looked around rather startled to see where he was and who was holding him. He made a move as if to strike for his freedom. But the exertion was too great for him, and he drooped again, his eyes closing and his head falling to Giny's fingers. Once more there was the desperate gasping. Giny shared her breath with him until there was fresh evidence of life. For many minutes this battle of life continued, the frail little creature passing close to the borderland, only to be brought back by Giny's efforts.

In the meantime I had examined him thoroughly and determined that there were no broken bones. He was suffering from shock, and if he could be brought through these first few minutes, there was a good chance that he might survive.

Our first real hopeful sign was when Urch gave a *peep* that was almost inaudible. He seemed somewhat inspired by his own voice. His eyes opened wide. "Peep!" he exclaimed again, which might have been the song-sparrow baby talk for "Where am I?"

"You are in the hands of friends, Urch," I said, delighted at the increasing signs of life. "This is Giny who saved you. But you can't marry her out of gratitude. I beat you to it. She didn't save my life, but she made it worth living. Now take it easy, little fellow. You couldn't be safer anywhere in the world than right here."

Urch had made several moves as if to get away, but he hadn't much strength. His eyes closed again, and Giny had to help him out once more with borrowed breath. We brought an eye dropper filled with water and put one drop down his throat. This called forth another peep, and he looked at us as if he were half convinced of our good intentions. We tried a drop of milk administered in the same way, then another and another. We were not sure just what should be done for a baby song sparrow who had been bopped on the top of his head. I guess no books have been written on the subject. But we were making progress. There was no question but that with each passing moment, the youngster was regaining strength. In fact, he was getting a little bit fresh. He pecked at my finger which was extended toward him with the friendliest of intentions.

Then suddenly he undertook to fly. Giny was unprepared for this, and her Urchin got away. His accomplishments were not in line with his ambitions, however. The most he could do with his tiny and tired wings was soften his fall to the floor. There he lay helplessly sprawled, as if he were a collection of feathers cut off last year's hat.

"Urch, you mustn't do that!" Giny said as she picked him up and held him to her cheek. "Now look, you have used up all your pep and we have to start over again!"

Urch's appearance filled us with concern. His eyes closed and his beak came open. Not even the gasping was evident. It looked as if this latest bump caused by his frantic efforts to be free had been more than he could stand.

Giny was not to be defeated. Steadily she gave her breath to her little patient, but more important still, she silently gave him of her faith. It seemed that he just couldn't come back this time. For many minutes there was not the slightest sign of life. Then to our delight, he gave a little gasp. Following this, he revived rather quickly, and his faint *peep* was one of the sweetest and most welcome sounds I have heard.

Giny was determined Urch should not leap to the floor

again, nor make any other move that might use up his precious bit of strength. She formed a sort of cage about him with her fingers, so that the air could go in but he couldn't get out. We decided that the best thing that could be done for him was to put him where he couldn't hurt himself, and where nothing else could hurt him. There he could stay while the healing forces of Nature operated within him. Accordingly, I obtained a cardboard box, spread a soft cloth on the bottom, cut air holes in the top and sides and placed him in it. With our ears to the sides we listened to learn how he was taking his confinement. The darkness and warmth seemed to be to his liking. We heard a dainty murmuring, perhaps a series of infantile *peeps,* as he accepted his private sanitorium in the spirit in which it was intended. And though he remained there all day long, I believe no ten minutes of it passed without one or the other of us listening or looking in to see how he was.

When Duke came back, we hastened to tell him what had happened. "Wait until you see Urch!" we exclaimed, as soon as our soldier had put his foot in the door.

"Wait until I see whom?"

"Urch—our little Urchin," I said.

Carefully we folded the top of the box back so Duke might look in—that is, if he could find room alongside our heads. There sat Urch in one corner, looking up at us in a nondescript manner. He was listing to one side a bit, as if one wing were affected by his rough experiences. While Duke touched him with his fingers and pelted him with baby talk, we told the story. Duke was delighted, and in his eyes was a look of tenderness that thrilled Giny and me.

"But hasn't he eaten all day?" asked Duke, up to his old tricks. Well we remembered how he had stuffed the Squints when they first arrived. "What's the idea? Urch is no ghost! He has to have food. Want me to go out and catch him some bugs or worms? Do I have to chew them up for him, as his mother would?"

"No, no, Duke!" we laughed. "But if you insist on his having food, maybe a little bread softened in milk would be welcome."

Duke had bread and milk ready so quickly it seemed as if he had been carrying them in his pocket. But it was one thing to provide the food, another to get Urch to eat it. The little fellow was accustomed to mighty fine service in his world. Not only was his food brought to him, it was partially chewed by his parents and then poked down his throat. All he had to do was swallow; he didn't even have to bite. Hence when Duke put the contribution before him, though it was served in fine style and consisted of Giny's homemade bread and Grade A milk, not a move would the little songster make to help himself. He just rose to his feet, stood there feebly, fluttered his wings and waited for someone to do something to help him. It was a problem, but we solved it at last. A pair of fine tweezers did the trick. With these, welcome bites could be tucked down his throat so far he could not do otherwise than accept them. And with each bite the baby developed more confidence and more interest in life in general. He was actually reaching for the offerings, and showing impatience if they were delayed.

Giny and I had realized much joy in this whole experience. It is so good to see a living thing that has within it the ability to add beauty to the world, beat the tricks of tragedy and chance. The triumph of this baby song sparrow was a victory for us as well.

Still, nothing in the whole adventure brought us greater joy than to see Duke feed the Urchin. It was reminiscent of the days when the Squints had first arrived over a year before. There sat the soldier, who had faced savagery running rampant, much concerned about the welfare of this mite of life. We saw him take the creature in his great hands, mindful of our warning about the little fellow's tendency to risk being hurt in an attempt to escape. We saw him pin the delicate baby wings in a way that held them firmly but without pressure. Then came small mouthfuls of the food, tenderly and thoughtfully administered. Our eyes did not rest on the feeding, however. They did not focus on the bird. Giny and I were fascinated by the look on Duke's face. There were kindliness, pity, compassion, tenderness—and something of a yearning perhaps that this sort of service might be his lot rather than that which the world imposed on him. And Giny and I exchanged looks that said what we could not put in words at that moment. Something still lived in our captain that we had feared might be a war casualty. This fineness of character, this Christly compassion for living things that were frail and in need of help, this strong gentleness had outlived the roar of unnumbered guns. It was more powerful than the hatred that was running amuck between nations. Duke could still lay all his strength and his love in service at the feet of a living thing in distress.

But Urch did not tarry with us long. When morning came, he knew it and was full of life. Not even the darkness of his box could restrain his ambitions. We heard him moving about as soon as the sun began tinting the eastern sky. At one moment he almost frightened us. We had placed his box on the table, and were standing near it trying to figure out the best way to release him. For obviously he belonged to the wilds. Out in the morning we heard a strange little bird cry—one that we did not recognize. But Urch did! That was Mother's voice, and oh, it sounded good! He let out a sharp note that would have done justice to a blue jay. Coming from the depths of the box right beside us, it startled us. It was like the squeak of a mouse over a public-address system—not that I have heard one but I can imagine how it would be. Urch was very much alive, and he wanted to get out in the world and prove it.

We decided we would set the box in the yard, open the cover, and if he could fly clear of the sides, he was ready to go out on his own again. It was a fair test as far as Urch was concerned. When he saw daylight as the box covers were being spread, he cleared the sides as if they were flat, and headed out through the trees in the direction from which his mother had called. One wing seemed a little weak, and he dropped to the ground once. But we did not have time to get to him. Up he went again, and he disappeared with a display of flying that convinced us we need not worry about him.

In later weeks, a song sparrow in his first year's plumage often came to the feeding station, with one of his wings trailing a little as he hopped. We felt sure it was our Urchin. And before he left at the end of the season, the little fellow repaid us for our trouble a thousand times in the coin of golden melodies.

XXVI

LIEUTENANT IN A KIMONO

THE old oak tree, in whose branches Eeny had once lived, had never looked on a lovelier campfire evening. A robin perched in its crest and in song foretold the close of day. The sturdy oak had stretched far its strong arms, and ruffled up its leafy locks in the last breeze of twilight. It had seen the evening star sparkling in the afterglow, and watched weary wavelets come to rest. A quiet cool that was close to frost settled like an invisible blanket over the northland and put all pestersome mosquitoes to sleep. Then out of dark distance came the call of bullfrogs, the voices of the night heron and the great barred owl.

The old oak had witnessed many such campfire parties. Through the years it had looked with leafy dignity on our fire-lighted circles, echoed our laughter and our songs and added silent counsel to our serious moments. Now again it had seen us gather with armloads of wood and baskets of food. It had seen friends come across the waters by boat and canoe, heard our greeting warm with friendship and seen us kneel to light the fire.

It was a momentous and distinctive evening, even though it was not meant to be. Really, it was supposed to be exactly like all the other campfire evenings before it, and like those to come. Duke wanted it that way. How would he like to spend his last evening at the Sanctuary? Why, just like the others, certainly not as though it were the last. His day should be devoted to wandering in the forest looking for adventure, his evening to a campfire gathering at the foot of the old oak—like those so often held there before.

He wanted north-woods companions there, and music, and happiness and food of the kind that fits such occasions best.

So it was that friends came to spend this campfire evening with our soldier—not the last, just the latest one, we all agreed. And in spite of wartime difficulties, we had found steaks to broil—thick, tender and juicy. Each friend who came had brought some miracle in a covered dish—salads, homemade rolls, potatoes done in secret and luscious ways, tasty puddings, delicious pies.

While hours sped by, the old oak tree watched these happy goings-on and in a sylvan way smiled down on us and entered into the fun. Possibly it saw some of the uninvited guests who crashed the party gate, but it gave us no warning. Up from the water's edge toward the firelight crept an awkward little figure, wet from a swim from the mainland. It moved through the ferns and low balsam boughs, until it peered unnoticed on the campfire circle. Then with a little low grunt, it turned to the darkness again, worked silently past the foot of the oak, around to where someone had placed a valued plate of food for a moment on a camp chair. Here the little visitor rose on its hind legs and sniffed at the tempting dinner. Parts of it were to his liking, and parts not. So with a heavily clawed foot he reached for his chosen bites and promptly pulled the whole plate of food off the chair, and upside down on the ground! Then came the discovery, mixed with dismay, that Salt, the old truant porcupine, had come to our gathering. All were on their feet at once, not only to greet our old pet, but to put plates, cups, dishes, skillets, wraps—and everything else that a porcupine could chew or tip over—far from his possible reach. Salt sat up, sniffed at the many hands that were reached to him in greeting, listened to the silly things that were said, and then began feasting on the dinner which was served him on the ground.

The oak tree said nothing of the numerous figures that later came from the water and circled us unnoticed while we drowned their soft footfalls with our singing. They too were dripping with water from their swim. They must have looked like little furry ghosts moving with such ease and purpose through the darkness, and gathering like a clan at the back door of the cabin. They found food to their liking, and it was from a spat over who should have the most of it that we learned of their presence. Giny took a flashlight and went to investigate. A moment later she called for Duke to come greet the guests. There were the two old raccoons, Rack and Ruin, who had so often come to our feeding station. But this time, as if out of tribute to our soldier, they had brought along their children, grandchildren and great-grandchil-

dren. There were a dozen or more coons, tumbling over one another, running under the house and out again, darting through the darkness and filling the island with life.

I had been watching Duke much throughout the day and evening. In spite of the fact that he wanted this day to "be like every other day," it was apparent that he could not disregard facts. This was his last full day at the Sanctuary. He had kept very busy during the daytime, but the events woven into the hours had farewells written in them. I saw him land at the point where Eeny had been located, and spend some time there. Then his canoe was on the beach near Mo's new-found land, and later at the shore of the country of Meeny and Miney. At the island he spent much time with Still-Mo, the chipmunks and Blooey, taking each creature through its stunts as if trying to fasten all this firmly in his memory.

At the campfire, Duke had entered everything with enthusiasm. He drank in the soft beauty of night, sang and joked with our friends. But as the evening wore on, I noticed that he became more and more quiet. He went apart from the group and sat near the limit of firelight, looking in silence at the star-filled sky. For a long time he stayed there, obviously in deep thought. When, presently, he returned to the circle his mood had sobered, and there was the faraway look in his eyes that had distressed us before. His lips were drawn tight over his teeth, and he seemed not to hear the comments and jibes that several friends hurled at him. Making his way over to the old oak, he leaned his back against it, folded his arms and with pre-occupied expression stared into the fire. For a few moments he seemed to have forgotten where he was, and that we were present.. Suddenly awakening from this, he realized he had been acting strangely, and he made an effort to rise out of the mood. How about some more music? he asked—and there was more music. He joined in the songs with forced cheerfulness.

But I could see that our captain had not been healed of the hidden scar of war.

There was a thinly covered heaviness in our entire group thereafter which led to an early break-up of the campfire party. Good nights and good lucks were said as the guests took their leave. They sang a little as they went out into the night in their several boats and canoes. The fire had been built up to light their way, and for the lovely scene they might look back on.

Giny, Duke and I stood looking into the quiet night, listening to the last faint sounds of our departing friends. Salt had resurrected himself from somewhere in the dark depths of the island and moved slowly up to our feet. However, he did not give his usual little grunt of greeting. We could hear the rustle of his quills as he walked awkwardly along, but he did not use his voice.

Then we realized that Nature had gone into one of her rare moods of absolute quiet. We speak of silence and solitude in relation to the natural world, and yet sound is generally present. It is simply sound that is not irritating, and we call it silence. But occasionally Nature does away with all that is audible; she stills the voices of her children with a kind of charm that she alone knows. Then in her sacred chambers there is not only silence and solitude—there is a miraculous quiet that carries with it a deep rest. What command is given to bring this profound hush is a secret of the ages. We only know that it happens. Such occasions are rare in our experience, so rare that we speak of them with reverence and awe. And when we stand as witnesses of this miracle in quiet we find we too are led by something within us to hold our voices and avoid even the slightest sound.

So the four of us, Salt included, stood on the shore of our island and marveled at the heavenly stillness in the ebony mansions of this north-woods night. At first, far out on the water faint in starlight, we could see the departing boats looking like floating shadows. But one at a time they disappeared around a point, as if the massive shades of the distant wooded shores had absorbed them. One canoe trailed the others slightly. Though it was nearly half a mile away, we could hear distinctly the drip of

water from its paddles. Then it too vanished into the hush
and mystery which ruled the wilderness. Now not a voice
was raised to break the spell—not one. It might be expected that one bullfrog might violate the decree of
nature, perhaps one raccoon might emit a single trill, one
coyote might try his lungs to hear his own echo, or one
nighthawk give his rasping call. But Giny, Duke, Salt
and I could not find even a whisper of a sound in the
infinite stillness about us. Not even the whirr of a wing,
the rustle of a leaf, the breaking of a wavelet on the shore
dared brave the dictum which governed this heavenly
moment. The children of Nature were listening with all
their being—listening, perchance, to a soft but omnipotent
voice which spoke within them, telling of things divine.
For one could not look on this marvelous moment without feeling that God was moving on the face of the waters
to bring about a Christly calm, and that all created things
knelt in silent prayer before Him.

We human beings seem unable to remain at high alti-
tudes long. For a few minutes we stood there fully at-
tuned, but then the rather noisy call of "things to be
done" was heard. Giny went to the cabin to begin straightening up the wholly happy disorder which follows a
campfire dinner. Duke, Salt and I remained behind to
straighten up the camp grounds, and finally to put out the
fire. Salt was his usual helpful self, getting right in my
way wherever I turned. Presently my attention was drawn
to Duke, who was half kneeling beside the fire, looking
vacantly at the glowing coals. His appearance startled

me. The expression on his face was so foreign to it that
had I not known for sure it was he, I could easily believe
a stranger had just arrived. He looked years older. His
lips were tightly drawn, his brow wrinkled, and he drew
his hand slowly across his forehead as if something there
pained him severely.

I went to him and put my arm across his broad shoulders. He seemed not to notice me.

"Duke, old boy," I said, "you haven't left it all in the
forest, have you? Something still gets you."

The soldier nodded his head.

"But sometimes we get rid of things by talking," I persisted. "Don't you want to bring it out, just put it in
words and see if we can't whip it that way?"

He nodded again, and yet said nothing, apparently not
knowing just where to begin.

"Let me see if I am right, Duke," I continued. "Is it
that you dread going back so terribly?"

He looked at me in intense seriousness. In words uttered slowly and in low voice to emphasize his point he
said, "I dread it so much, I wonder if I have turned—
yellow," and he shook his head a little when he said the
last word, as if it gave physical pain.

"Duke, don't talk like that!" I exclaimed. "You know
that isn't true. You know you will face whatever is before
you, and do whatever duty demands. You *know* that, don't
you?"

Duke thought for a moment. "Yes, I suppose I will.
But why should I dread it so? Others go back into it, and

while no one likes it, they don't feel the way I do. And it doesn't seem to be the fighting that I think of, it is——"

He was quiet for a moment.

"Just what is it, Duke?" I asked, trying not to make the sympathy I felt too obvious. "Come on, let's name it and we'll know what to fight."

Duke was thinking hard. "I have tried to do that. It seems to be something I can't get hold of. It feels as if I were going into something vast and entirely empty. It isn't what is there that I fear; it is what isn't there. Just a great dark night with nothing in it. Sounds silly, but that is the picture that haunts me. I can't get rid of it."

Duke had risen and stood rubbing one closed fist against the palm of his other hand. The fire was losing itself in ashes, and far and wide the forest's mood of silence still prevailed. Then came the faint sound made by dripping paddles. We looked out into the night, and when the firelight had left our eyes we saw the last canoe was returning to us.

"There is some mail for you," called one from the canoe. "Had it in my pocket and forgot to give it to you. I'm glad we did, because it gave us an excuse for more canoeing."

Greetings flew back and forth, and we made friendly but somewhat uncomplimentary remarks about their forgetfulness, and comments on the previous silence of the night. Duke and I met them at the water's edge where they presented us with letters, several for our captain. He went to read them by the firelight.

Our friends in the canoe started away again, to enjoy more of the still night, they said. But they had very little opportunity. Suddenly the mood of nature was abruptly changed. There was sound in the air, lots of it, and it went bouncing around the shores in echoes that grew louder and louder. In times past I have had a horror of anything breaking up the quiet in nature. Giny and I even avoid a whisper. But the sharp, startling, persistent sound that came to me then was the most beautiful music I have ever heard, I believe. I can't describe it. Maybe if you could get a dozen kingfishers, three or four wild geese, a turkey gobbler, and some red squirrels to indulge their wildest chattering all at once, it might be something like it. I don't know. But I repeat, I had never heard anything more welcome or truly beautiful. I fairly ran toward the campfire.

There was Duke, all entangled in an old-time cackle spasm! His arms were wrapped around his midsection as he bent over in near hysterics, and he gave out those peals of laughter that seemed to start at his feet and go all the way to the top of his head. Involuntarily I let out the war whoop that I reserve for occasions of great joy. It bounced around the shores, too, and silence was even less than a memory. But if nature didn't like it, it was just too bad. To hear Duke break loose was the answer to my deepest prayer.

There were calls from the departing canoeists asking what was going on, and if we needed help. I assured them everything was under control—somewhat.

But Duke had got hold of himself enough to make explanations, and they were certainly in order. Giny had come from the cabin, and we stood together laughing at him, and waiting to know what was up.

"Listen to this! Listen to this!" cried Duke, so excited each word stepped on the heels of the one before it. He was holding a letter in his hand and trying to see it clearly in spite of low firelight and tears in his eyes.

Then in sentences that were often broken by outbursts of laughter, he revealed to us a story akin to many in the world. It was a letter from an Army pal. The boy had been presumably lost on the raid in which Duke was hurt. He was missing for a time, and then showed up again. In the meantime, he had been cared for by native guerrillas.

"But listen to this!" Duke fairly shouted. We were listening all over.

"He saw the Loot—Lieutenant Still-Mo—he saw him!" Duke was shaking with excitement, and we were too. "The Loot wasn't hurt a bit, except in his feelings. He's still back in the islands somewhere with the guerrillas. And what do you think——"

Here Duke lost himself in another outburst of laughter. It was just like old times. He pounded his chest and stamped his feet. We waited rather impatiently for him to get ready to tell us more.

"The Loot was dressed in a *kimono!*" It was all Duke could do to get that last word out. His voice broke into a long series of haw-haws!

Then he began dressing up his story. The Loot had his clothes destroyed during the action. The only thing the guerrillas had that would fit him was that dress. Duke could hardly stand it. Why, the Loot's neck was *that big*— he measured off the size of a stovepipe. Still-Mo's arms were as big as hams, he said, and his muscles looked like a boa that has swallowed a pig. Think of all *that* in a kimono!—and Duke was lost in another spasm.

"It couldn't have been a kimono," laughed Duke. "It must have been a tent." With many a call of "woo-woo" he demonstrated with a sissy-strut how the Loot would parade about, how he would do a hula dance, powder his nose and pluck his eyebrows. "And he's so tough you couldn't drive a nail in him," our soldier raved on. "I might have known a little dynamite couldn't dent his carcass—the rascal!"

The leaves of the ancient oak rustled a little in a newly born forest breeze. The campfire perished in a cloud of steam as a pail of water extinguished its last embers. Nature had withdrawn its decree of silence, and little voices spoke in the forest depth. An osprey was crying somewhere in the distance, and the old owl called as if he were talking in a rain barrel. Salt slipped into the water and swam away on some secret mission. The last of the raccoons had left.

Duke sang a little song as he went to bed. His letter had been read to ribbons. Late into the night we heard him giving little phrases of laughter as he recalled again the story it had brought. But we knew this was not just amusement. There was really nothing so funny about Lieutenant Still-Mo dressed in a kimono. Duke was just supremely happy, that was all.

XXVII

A SUPER-NUT WITH WHISKERS

THE summer's hair was now turning gray. Grasses on the hillside had lost their green under the constant heat of August days. Birds had about finished their nesting, and feathered youths were undergoing thorough schooling from their parents. Eeny, Meeny, Miney, Mo and Still-Mo, in their various home countries about the shores, were beginning autumn industry. Chipmunks, blue jays, grackles and redwings increased their interest in our feeding station. Salt and Pepper had not been seen for a long time. It may be that they had wandered far, or possibly their summer laziness had developed to such a degree that they settled down in one spot without the energy to move. When Salt was last seen he looked as if this might happen. Several times we saw little Urch. One wing still hung down a bit, but he flew well and we felt sure he would be able to tag along when his family started its flight south.

Duke was once more "somewhere in the South Pacific." He had spent several days with his family as his leave came to a close, and then headed back to service. We knew Duke's problem had been met. He was more than ready to go—he was anxious. "I *must* go now," he had said.

225

"And the quicker the better. Who knows? Maybe I can land right where the Loot is. If I can find those little Squints in the forest like the one up there, I ought to be able to find that big bum—in a kimono." And we felt that if he did, we would hear echoes of the resulting cackle spasm wherever we were.

A gift box arrived one day addressed:

> Mr. Still-Mo Squint Red Squirrel
> In care of the Campbells
> Three Lakes, Wisconsin

The return address showed it came from Duke. We opened it eagerly with many a giggle and a guess as to what it contained. But all guesses were wrong. In it was a large round object wrapped in tissue paper and tied with bright-colored ribbon, Christmas-present style. There was even a gift card enclosed. It read:

> To Stubby-tailed Still-Mo:
> Roses are red,
> Violets are blue.
> Sweets to the sweet—
> And nuts to you!

We unwrapped the ribbon and tissue paper to find a big coconut, a gift of doubtful value for a red squirrel.

Giny called Still-Mo, and soon the little bright-eyed fellow came hopping from tree to tree, and down to the ground near us. The coconut lay ominously on the ground. He took no notice of it at first, but came directly to our feet looking up as if to ask what all the shouting was about. He could not understand why we stood there doing nothing about it. What was the big idea of calling him from his work if all we wanted to do was stand and stare at him!

Giny tossed a peanut to the ground right beside the coconut. When Still-Mo raced over to pick it up, he spied this great big thing that looked like a large be-whiskered super-nut. He backed up to get a better look at it. He had never seen anything like it before, and probably doubted if anyone else ever had. Even the tall tales his parents may have told him about the size of nuts that grew when they were children couldn't equal this thing before him. He sat up and rubbed his face with his forepaws, as if he couldn't believe his eyes. But when he looked again, there was the nut and it was just as big as he was afraid it was. Maybe this was some kind of trick. Perhaps those low-down blue jays had rigged up a trap for him. He began advancing toward it with his typical caution, a step at a time, and chirping a challenge. Finally his nose was up to it, and apparently the scent was to his liking. Fear left him. He put his front feet against it, and tried to take a bite of the funny-looking thing. His jaws wouldn't spread wide enough to let his teeth get contact. He looked at it with puzzled expression, and tried another bite. Still no luck. He scratched hard at it with his front feet, but not a dent could he make.

In desperation he jumped on top of it and tried again to bite into it. Then the coconut began to roll! Still-Mo

jumped for dear life. This made the nut roll back a little, and then it came right at him faster than ever. He hadn't seen anything like that since he was attacked by the milk bottle weeks ago. There was no time to think, for the great big thing was coming. Away he went at top speed. Unfortunately Still-Mo chose to run downhill, and the coconut fairly charged after him. For a moment it seemed as if it might run over him, but he swerved to one side and disappeared under the shed. The coconut banged loudly against the boards as if eager to take one last wallop at him, and there it rested. A moment later Still-Mo stuck his little nose out to learn about conditions, and spied the whopper nut not three inches away. With a shriek, he vanished again, and did not return until almost nighttime.

When Giny and I had recovered from our laughter, we took the nut, drained and drank its juice and then broke it open with a hammer. Later Still-Mo was presented with some of the meat. But whether it was not to his liking, or because he did not trust the nut after the way it had acted, he refused to take even a bite. Possibly he thought food that goes chasing a fellow couldn't be very tasty. He sniffed at it, perhaps just to make sure the thing wouldn't or couldn't take after him again, but he wanted none of it.

We wrote a letter to Duke telling him the gift had arrived, and what a panic it caused. Still-Mo refused to add a postscript of gratitude.

XXVIII

CARRY ON!

THE forest world went on about its busy living. Everywhere was the hum of seasonal activity. The first touch of autumnal splendor was appearing in the trees. Another summer had passed, another fall was beginning, another winter just beyond, another spring over the horizon. In the measureless vaults of nature there is an endless supply of seasons to deck the world with interest and loveliness throughout ages to come.

Giny and I found time to be on the trails occasionally. We visited our rediscovered Squints and saw with satisfaction that they were preparing ably for their second winter in the north country. We searched and searched for the valley where Duke had seen the old porcupine Inky. We hoped that the summer might grant us just one more miracle and let us find our valued friend. We found many valleys which seemed to fit in with Duke's description of the place where Inky had come to him, but our bequilled old friend did not respond to our calls.

There came a day when I wished that I had some mystic power wherewith I might call all the creatures about us for a few moments. There was something I wanted to share with them. I would choose for our meeting a cer-

tain hillside that forms a natural amphitheater and gather
in the woodsfolk from far and wide. I would want Eeny,
Meeny, Miney, Mo and Still-Mo there in the front row,
if they could stop their bantering with one another long
enough. Near them I would place Stubby, Beggar Boy,
Mrs. Beggar Boy, Junior and the other chipmunks of the
island—though, while I was wishing, I had better wish
for a stone wall to put between them and the Squints. I
would want old Blooey and his blue-feathered relatives to
perch in a convenient tree—and shut up (for goodness
sake!) and listen. I would call the great eagle that soars
close to the clouds, the deer that graces the shore line,
birds that sing at eventide, with all other creatures, trees

and plants, so that I might read them a certain invaluable
letter from Duke. And if microphones were at hand to
carry his word over international networks, it would be
better still.

It was a sort of thank-you letter. Duke had thanked Giny and me until we were embarrassed—we were grateful to have served him in any way, and it seemed little enough to do for a lad who was giving the world so much. He said:

"Expressing gratitude seems to help finish the blessings I have received. Please, if you get the chance, thank all those little guys that live in the woods, the woods themselves, the trails and lakes, and the solitude that rests there. Only now am I realizing fully what they did for me. *They brought me close to God!*"

There is the message I wanted to read to chattering, jabbering, rushing little folk of the forest. They had taken part in a miracle. Their very presence had contributed to the greatest blessing a man may know in life— being brought *"close to God!"* It is probable that all people and creatures who live up to their highest ideals are vastly more important than they realize. A great half-hidden purpose is being fulfilled in the world. And trees with their busy leaf-growing, flowers with their blooming, birds with their singing and nest-building, squirrels and chipmunks with their nut-gathering—all add up to a magnificent influence which summons forth the thought of God, near and dear. What a glorious thing they have done!

Duke expresses the message I would have for that woodland congregation:

"The days I spent alone on the Sanctuary trails deep in the forest—what treasures they are! They stay alive and vivid. I have my notebook written there, and I read from it constantly. Nothing that I saw or experienced must get away from me. It is a sort of super K-ration that I feed on when the mental diet here is filled with confusion.

"You must have known all along that I wasn't just out on solo picnics up there. I had a grand time at the hiking and wandering around, but there was more to it than that. Something in my thought had to be settled. I don't know just how to put it, but maybe you will understand this—*I had to know how I stand with God.* What little I knew of Him seemed to leave Him so far away. The effect of prayer had been proved to me, but it gave me no comfort to think of us mortals being in a mixed-up, trouble-filled world, even though He would help us if we just got desperate and prayed loud enough.

"But out in the woods I began to realize that the feeling of separation was in myself, nowhere else. Everything I did made me feel closer to Him. I prayed without ceasing, not for some special blessing or favor but just to understand. And the answer came to me when I touched those mounds of cushion moss, when I walked among trees, felt them close, intimate and friendly with me. The very touch of my feet upon the earth increased this feeling of oneness with the Creator. Even rain pelting down upon me brought me closer.

"Then came the day old Inky walked up to me so friendlylike. This was natural, real, and it made all the rough, savage and cruel things seem unnatural, against the grain of nature. The imagined space between God and me largely disappeared that day in the little valley— where I left your compass."

If old Inky were in our fancied forest audience and heard this I can imagine his reaction. He always looked so complacent and self-sufficient anyway. He would chatter his teeth a little, shake up his quills and look up as if to say, "Aw, balsam juice! How in a hemlock could you ever feel far from God? You humans make me sick, you get so involved and tangled. You couldn't get separated from your Creator any more than a sunbeam can get away from the sun!"

Duke's letter was filled with thoughts worth while.

"There is one tiny violet I would like to thank and thank," he said. "It was somewhere on a hillside to the east of Vanishing Lake. Just tell it that it brought me into a feeling of humility that I wish everyone in the world might experience. That day I sat on the hillside to eat every last crumb of the fine lunch lovely Giny had given me. Then near my feet, so close I had nearly stepped on it, I discovered that tiny little violet, just poking its head up through the old leaves. I remember saying aloud, 'You have a lot of crust coming up in a big world like this!' Then I began looking closely at it. It seemed to me that some new kind of a light shone on it and brought out more beauty than I had ever noticed before. Of course, it was just my own thought awakening, but it was so sudden I couldn't understand it at first. The color and form of the little flower were simply amazing. Its beauty was so captivating, I said, 'Little guy, how *do* you do it?'

"I guess I didn't expect an answer, but I got one. It came as the realization that the flower didn't do *anything!* It wasn't its own creator. It was the beautiful result of some power vastly greater than itself.

"Strange how things come to a fellow at a time like that. I haven't read Scripture much, not nearly so much as I should have, but I remembered instantly the words 'I can of mine own self do nothing.' How that applied to the violet, to the trees, to me, and to everything in the universe! I can't carry the idea much farther without talking over my head, but certainly it was clear to me then that this world is the work of God—and while I am part of His creation, I can't even make a violet.

"Everything took on a new and higher importance to me after that—our Squints, chipmunks, birds, porkies and all things that go to make up this world. Each living thing is a lesson, a parable to be understood, something we can go by and grow by. Boy! What a different look the world has when you see it that way, and how close the Creator is to His creation!

"But do you know I couldn't quite accept all this until word came that the Loot was alive. I guess I would have got beyond the hump sometime or other by thinking and praying on. But it seemed the Loot just had to be with me and I couldn't give him up. We have been through a

lot together, and the old boy rings true every step of the
way. A world without him looked mighty empty. But
when word came that he was OK, it finished the picture
for me.

"I am determined to hold onto all this faith that the
forest has helped me gain. For I have the conviction that
this is what every one of us must do sometime, some way—
find out how he stands with God. What happens in war
or in peace depends on that. And I wish everyone in the
world could go alone out on forest trails, just looking and
listening to nature for days as I did. It is a way to find
God so close to yourself that you are one with Him."

Then Duke's letter told of plans—plans that sounded
real and wonderfully close. When the job was done, he
wanted to come back to those same forest trails. He would
bring Lieutenant Still-Mo—kimono and all! They would
dive into the solitude and stay until their thoughts were
washed free of the scars of war.

"For," wrote Duke, "we will need the sanity of nature
for our work in peace even more than in war. The re-
sponsibility will be even greater. Our problem now is in
a war that is man-made. When this nightmare is done,
we want to get back into the world that God made until
its sweet influence teaches us how to live. Please, keep
it ready for us."

And there is your commission, all you nature folk. That
is why I wanted to call you together. Go on about your
growing, your living, all of which make up such a wonderful world. Duke, and the many like him, are going to

need you. Eeny, Meeny, Miney, Mo and Still-Mo, smooth out your coats and rehearse your funniest capers! Inky, Salt and Pepper, waddle around and practice being porcupines! All you birds and beasts, get busy at your woodland lives! You trees and flowers, you sunsets and dawns, you stars and rainbows that make life lovely, live on in increasing splendor! You mountains, hills, valleys, lakes and streams, get out your grandeur! Enrich all solitude, deepen all silence. It is within your sacred power to point the thoughts of tired people to God.